The Ruff

*For my teacher
Gerard Baerends*

The Ruff

Individuality in a gregarious
wading bird

By

JOHAN G. VAN RHIJN

Illustrated by
IAN WILLIS

T. & A.D. POYSER
London

© *Johan G. van Rhijn 1991*

ISBN 0–85661–062–3

First published in 1991 by T & A.D. Poyser Ltd
24–28 Oval Road, London NW1 7DX

United States Edition published by
ACADEMIC PRESS INC.
San Diego, CA 92101

Text set in Times
Typeset by Paston Press, Loddon, Norfolk
Printed and bound in Great Britain by
Mackays of Chatham PLC, *Chatham, Kent*

British Library Cataloguing in Publication Data
Rhijn, Johan G. van
  The ruff.
  1. Ruffs
  I. Title
  598.33

  ISBN 0–85661–062–3

Contents

List of Photographs

List of Figures

List of Tables

Preface

Before I started to write this book, the Ruff was the main subject in at least 60 publications, comprising scientific and popular articles and also books; altogether about 1600 pages of text, written by roughly 55 different authors. Also, the Ruff clearly featured in a much larger number of publications, in which it played a role of secondary importance. Thus, the Ruff received a remarkable citation score for a single species.

I was the author of seven of these publications, both scientific and popular, mainly on social organization, totalling about 125 pages of text. This new book about the Ruff is neither a reiteration of my own research data in rather more words, nor a compilation of known facts from the literature. My main intention is to integrate facts and ideas about the Ruff, mainly with respect to its social behaviour. I have tried to make it interesting not only for professional ornithologists, ecologists, ethologists, and sociobiologists, but also for enthusiastic bird watchers.

To interest the professionals, I have to offer something new. In fact, this was the least difficult job. By writing a book I have been able to include many minor details which are not very interesting on their own, but thought-provoking in a broader perspective. I have also been able to connect diverse facts which have not been associated before. Their combination offers new insights, for instance on wader migration.

To hold the attention of those who watch birds just as a hobby, I have had to be very careful in the way I described things. This has presented the greatest difficulties. Certain conclusions and ideas can hardly be transmitted in simple words. Yet, I do hope that the form in which facts and ideas are presented in this book help to elucidate them. I first want to take my readers with me into the field, to become acquainted with the bird, with its social organization, and with my approach to these subjects. Although the early chapters contain a lot of information, and new information too, they can easily be assimilated. Later chapters may become somewhat more complex, but, with a bit more effort and the experience gained from reading the first chapters, they should also be quite easy to follow. I hope that amateur bird watchers will also enjoy reading them and learning more about the Ruff.

My study on the Ruff has greatly benefited from the help of many people. My teacher Gerard Baerends encouraged me, and corrected many wild ideas, but always gave free play to scientific creativity. Lidy Hogan-Warburg, who studied

Ruffs before me, showed a lot of interest in my work, was always willing to discuss the species and other topics, and offered quite a number of fruitful ideas. New ideas also came from a discussion group on lek behaviour in which Jaap Kruijt, Eddy Bossema, Gerrit de Vos, the late Gavin Johnstone, Helga Gwinner, the late Dick Thalen, Freek Niewold, Gert Baeyens, and Johan de Jong participated. Part of the work on Ruffs was done by students. Martien Baars, Tineke de Boer, and Mechteld Leenknegt took part in the fieldwork, and Yolanda Holthuijzen and Bert van Dijk carried out experiments in the laboratory. Of course, my study could have never been completed without the cooperation of several cattle-breeders, who allowed the use of fields in which the mating areas were located. In addition, Staatsbosbeheer and the Rijksdienst voor de IJsselmeerpolders were very kind in giving me permission to study Ruffs in their sanctuaries.

Further development of my ideas was guided by discussions and correspondence with Detlev Drenckhahn, Amelia Segre (Terkel), L.N. Dobrinskij, Julia Shepard, Joop Brinkkemper, Robert Gibson, Albert Beintema, Jack Bradbury, Horst Meesenburg, John Maynard Smith, Maarten Frankenhuis, Andrzej Elzanowski, Pavel Tomkovich, Frank McKinney, Theunis Piersma, Klaas Koopman, David Lank, Connie Smith, Wendy Hill, Gerwin Meijer, and many others. The task of finally assembling and polishing the book was greatly helped by Andrew Richford, Euan Dunn and another reader. Parts of the manuscript have been read and improved by Lidy Hogan-Warburg, Amelia Terkel (Segre), Theunis Piersma, Klaas Koopman, Gabriëlle van Dinteren, and David Lank. Amelia Terkel, Gabriëlle van Dinteren and David Lank kindly gave me permission to use their unpublished data. Johannes Melter sent provisional data on wintering Ruffs in Senegal, collected by the O.A.G. of Münster. Wibe Altenburg, David Lank, Theunis Piersma and Arie Spaans drew my attention to important publications. Klaas Koopman compiled the most recent data on Ruffs trapped in Friesland and North Holland. Joop Brinkkemper supplied a number of splendid photographs. The present book would not have been published without the help of all these people. I wish to express my deep gratitude to them.

JOHAN VAN RHIJN

Displaying Ruffs in a typical Dutch meadow landscape, drawn by Hermann Schlegel (1861).

CHAPTER 1

Introduction

The Ruff *Philomachus pugnax* is a wader, most closely related to the arctic sandpipers. It breeds in northwestern Europe and in northern Asia. The species is migratory. Wintering occurs in Africa, in southwestern Asia, and in western and southern Europe.

The Ruff distinguishes itself from most other species of birds by its mating pattern. Males gather on display sites or *leks* which are visited by females for copulation. Only females care for the offspring. The degree of sexual dimorphism is considerable. Males are much larger than females and possess brilliantly coloured nuptial plumage (ruffs and head-tufts), whereas females are well camouflaged. This clear distinction led to the use of different terms for males and females: *ruffs* and *reeves*. Besides sexual dimorphism, the species is marked by extreme diversity of nuptial plumage, especially among males.

Ruffs compete on the leks for matings by behaving aggressively towards each other, or, alternatively, in certain individuals, by behaving submissively towards other males. Some ruffs, called *resident males*, having mainly dark plumage, defend small mating territories. Other males, called *marginal males*, having the same plumage types, visit the lek, do not defend such territories, but may occasionally show aggressive behaviour. These individuals may obtain the status of resident male during another phase of their life. Conversely, resident males may become marginal males. For this reason both types have been classified together as *independent males*. Quite distinct from these are the *satellites*, who are mainly white. They do not fight, but are parasitic on the mating territories. The status of independent and satellite male is not interchangeable. The difference between these two major classes of males seems to be partly based on genetic factors.

History

Although Linnaeus' naming of the Ruff *Tringa pugnax* was inspired by its behaviour, the earliest descriptions contain almost no information about ecology and behaviour. For instance, in the first edition of his *Manuel d'Ornithologie*, published in 1815, the ornithologist Temminck laid emphasis on systematic position and morphology. He gave no details of behaviour and presented only a few indications of the Ruff's habitat choice:

> 'lives in moist and marshy pastures; in spring never at the seashore; migrating flocks in autumn in the coastal area; nowhere as abundant as in Holland' (page 410, translated from the French).

Temminck's successor Schlegel, however, had an open mind regarding other characteristics. In his book on the birds of the Netherlands, published in 1861, the sixth plate shows birds in a meadow, including a small mating ground with six displaying ruffs and one reeve. Schlegel (1861) further remarks:

> 'They return in April to their breeding areas in the Netherlands. At that time the neck feathers of the males are not yet fully developed, but nevertheless a male soon prefers to become a member of a group, of four to eight individuals, which settles at a permanent site on the bank or margin of a ditch or a lake. There, the males regularly fight with each other. This fighting is accompanied by postures with an expanded ruff and with the bill directed towards the opponent. During fights ruffs rarely hurt each other. This peculiar scene can also be observed in captive individuals. For the rest, the Ruff is a silent, lonely, and shy bird' (page 176, translated from the Dutch).

Pioneers

The first person to take a real interest in the behaviour of the Ruff was an English ornithologist, Edmond Selous. He was guided by a Dutch schoolteacher, Jacob Thijsse, to the polder Het Noorden on the island of Texel. Thijsse was a very popular writer on animals, plants and nature conservation. He advised his readers, should they happen to spend Whit Sunday on the island of Texel, to take a cab and drive in the very early morning through the polders. They would then be able to approach the Ruffs to within 10 m and to see all their 'dancing'. Selous observed the behaviour of Ruffs at these mating grounds during spring 1906 from a small hiding-place made of turf. His primary goal was to find evidence in the field for Charles Darwin's theory of sexual selection. The marvellous diary describing how Selous was carried off to his shelter, his cold feet, the behaviour of other birds, and the strategy of reeves for selecting a mating partner, all interwoven with his thoughts about sexual selection, was published in six episodes in the *Zoologist* (1906–1907). This diary contains a lot of information about behaviour, and Selous' qualities as an observer emerge from his hinting at the existence of different male mating strategies.

Selous' 'pilgrimage' to the Ruffs at Texel was followed by a photographic expedition to the same place in spring 1920 by Miss E.L. Turner. She exposed six dozen plates in three days, with, unfortunately, only ten satisfactory results. The rest showed 'nothing but a smudge', because of the enormous liveliness of the birds. Six of her photographs were published in *British Birds*, accompanied by some notes in which she expressed her amazement at their 'ridiculous manner of behaving', and in which she wondered about the 'meaning of this extraordinary behaviour'.

It was to take until 1952 before Selous' understanding of the community of the Ruffs was equalled and improved by two Danish students, Peter Bancke and Horst Meesenburg, who spent several periods of 24 hours or more in a tent close to the mating grounds. Their study area was at Tipperne, a salt marsh peninsular in Ringkøbing fjord, which was, until 1931, connected with the North Sea. When the open connection was still there, the whole area could be inundated during high tides and storms. After this fjord was closed, a population of a few dozen Ruffs settled at Tipperne. Their natural history and population dynamics had been studied in the 1940s by F. Søgaard Andersen, Bancke and Meesenburg's teacher.

By watching the Ruffs uninterruptedly at the courtship area, which they called a *hill*, Bancke and Meesenburg discovered that many of the visiting males defended a small piece of land. Each territory, which they called a *run*, was mostly distinguished by a bare piece of earth, 30–60 cm in diameter. The distance between the centres of neighbouring runs was about 1 m. Territory owners appeared to be present during almost the whole day and copulations were only seen on these runs. Bancke and Meesenburg also discovered that several other males were visiting the hill for much shorter periods. Some of them remained at the border, but a few entered the runs and were tolerated by the owners. By means of very precise descriptions of all individuals, Bancke and Meesenburg were able to establish that particular individuals were only visiting the border, although they could try to settle or to conquer a run, while other individuals were always entering runs, without being bound to particular ones. The latter type of individual was tolerated by the owners and possessed a white or light plumage. Thus, the various roles played by the ruffs on a hill seemed to be fixed for the different individuals.

A proper understanding

In 1966 a new milestone was reached in the understanding of Ruff behaviour. This was due to the publication of Lidy Hogan-Warburg's study, which was mainly based on observations at the Dutch island Schiermonnikoog. Her data supported Bancke and Meesenburg's conclusions:

'Within a courting group of ruffs three different types of roles for individuals can be distinguished; the type of role is to a greater or lesser extent determined for each individual.'

Hogan-Warburg introduced another, somewhat less confusing, terminology than that proposed by Bancke and Meesenburg. A short introduction of her terms might be helpful because they will be used throughout this book.

The courting area was called a *lek*, which is derived from the Scandinavian word for 'play'. The leks are also visited by the reeves. Most courtship and mating occurs on these leks. Territorial males were called *resident males*. They stay during the main part of the day and defend bare sites of ground on the lek, the *residences*. Incidental or irregular visitors at the border of the lek were called *marginal males*. The birds who were visiting the territory owners, and were tolerated by them, received the name *satellite*.

Besides this support for earlier research, Hogan-Warburg presented a wealth of data on social organization and behaviour. She established that the status of a resident male may be interchanged with that of a marginal male; a resident male may lose its residence and a marginal male is a potential possessor. The status of a satellite male, however, seemed to be fixed for its whole life. In fact she distinguished between two main behavioural categories of males: a combined resident–marginal category, called *independent males*, and the *satellite* category. Independent males were found to possess mainly dark-coloured plumage, while the satellite plumage types usually appeared to be white or light coloured. In view of the constancy of status, and the strong relationship between status and plumage colour, she suggested that the distinction between independent males and satellites was based upon genetic differences. The maintenance of both types in a population should be based on a balanced polymorphism, which would result in fairly constant proportions of satellite and independent males in the population, and should be associated with appropriate reproductive potentials.

Another merit of Hogan-Warburg is her very precise description of behaviour patterns. She convincingly showed that there were clear differences between the behaviour of independent males and the behaviour of satellites, partly because the frequency of the different behaviour patterns differed between both categories, but also because the incidence of comparable behaviour patterns was dissimilar for the two categories. Independent males displayed much aggression, including fighting, or submissive behaviour, whereas satellites performed much behaviour which was sexually oriented.

Chance or choice?

I was the immediate successor of Lidy Hogan-Warburg, but it was by the merest accident. During a cycling trip in the neighbourhood of Groningen, I noticed that on the gates of a large number of adjoining meadows were nailed boards with the text: 'No entrance – breeding area for meadow birds'. If these boards had not been there, I never would have thought of entering, but immediately I became curious and asked a farmer about the ornithological importance of these fields. He told me about the various species of birds breeding there: Lapwing, Black-tailed Godwit, Redshank, Mallard, Garganey, Moorhen, Coot, Black Tern and Ruff. If I would like to visit the area, I should contact the local schoolteacher. At that time I was an undergraduate student in biology. I had attended several lectures in ethology and ecology by Professor Baerends, who was to become my main teacher. These lectures made a strong impression on me, and had inspired me to make my own observation tent to watch birds in their natural surroundings. Unfortunately I did not have a specific goal for my observations, but after talking with the farmer I began to develop one.

A few days later I visited the local schoolteacher. He asked me whether my desire to look around these meadows was connected with the Ruffs who maintained at least two mating grounds there. His question was prompted because somebody else, a certain Miss Warburg, had visited for the same purpose. At that moment I had no definite objective, so I answered that I wanted to observe various species of meadow birds, but immediately I also realized that these Ruffs would become my special interest. This thought was not inspired by the fact that I knew Miss Warburg (later Lidy Hogan-Warburg) slightly and had heard about her work on the Ruff during an excursion to the island of Schiermonnikoog. My idea arose in fact from the possibility of abandoning the vague plan of observing birds in their natural surroundings, in exchange for a realistic, specific research project. So, when I entered the meadows for the first time in spring 1964, I immediately carried my hide to the place where I was told I would find the Ruffs. After finding the birds, I erected the tent about 30 m away. After sitting in it for only a few minutes, the Ruffs returned to their mating place and resumed displaying, threat behaviour, and fighting. The whole scene absorbed all my attention. I stayed the whole afternoon, and returned on a dozen other occasions that season. During those visits I made descriptions of the birds, tried to make maps of their spatial distribution and took quite a lot of photographs. I really became obsessed, and when the season was over I started to think right away about the possibilities of continuing my observations the following year.

In 1965 the situation became ideal for me to start a study on Ruff behaviour. In the late winter and the very early spring I gained some experience with the behaviour of another bird displaying on leks, the Black Grouse. I had offered to help somebody for a few weeks in catching and marking these splendid birds. It was a first attempt, and I had moderate success. In theory I had to study for an important examination, but somewhat later I also paid a dozen visits to the displaying Ruffs. I had the time of my life, and perhaps that was the reason why I passed my exam. A successful examination meant that the period of learning facts and techniques was over and that a period with short research projects would start. I had arranged that all my research should be devoted to the Ruffs and towards understanding their behaviour and population genetics. In a conversation with Lidy Hogan-Warburg, who had finished her observations, the most promising direction of further research was traced out. Another factor also had a positive influence on my future study: I became involved with teaching at the University and got the opportunity to guide undergraduate students through a course in animal behaviour.

During the next three years I divided my energy between experiments with fruitflies in the Institute of Genetics, observations on Ruffs in the sanctuary for meadow birds, and transcribing, ordering and analysing field data and teaching students in the Zoology Department. I became more and more enthusiastic about this beautiful meadow bird which displayed on leks. My own observation tent played host to other, more professional tents belonging to the laboratory, and I received several visitors, including the late David Lack with his whole family. By the time I was prepared for another examination, Professor Baerends asked me to continue my study on the Ruff for a doctor's degree. Thus, I got the opportunity to deepen my pilot study, particularly on the function and evolution of the differentiation between independent males and satellites.

The scope of this book

This will not be a handbook of the Ruff. Detailed accounts of almost all aspects of this species are given by Glutz von Blotzheim and associates, by Cramp and Simmons, and, most recently, by Scheufler and Stiefel. The only thing I can add to these accounts is my personal experience. This book is written from that experience, from my own research, but is not restricted to it. During my fieldwork on Ruffs, and also later, while processing the data and doing other research, I became concerned with the literature on certain aspects of this species and on subjects which were related to my work on Ruffs. These studies will also form part of this book. Moreover, during and after my work on Ruffs, I became directly concerned with related research by other people on the same species or on a similar subject. That work, too, will be included, where it is relevant. Nonetheless, there are many aspects of the Ruff which will hardly be discussed in this book. This does not mean that they are not interesting: only that I do not feel able to add anything new about these aspects, and that they do not form an essential part of my story.

The function and evolution of the Ruff's behavioural dimorphism will be the main theme of this book, because I became most engaged with these topics. The organization of the book reflects the development of my knowledge of the species. Thus, I shall first give a detailed account of the Ruff's social organiz-ation and its courtship behaviour displayed on leks. The importance of these leks will come up in many ways. The book includes much material about the activities of the different types of males, and also about their interrelationships, which seem to be very delicately balanced. Satellite males are dependent on the residences owned by resident males for copulations. Conversely, resident males may attract more reeves to their residences by accepting satellites. Special attention will be paid to the factors influencing the reproductive success of males.

In some places the discussion must necessarily become quite detailed to provide a clear explanation of the argument. In order to serve both the general and more specialist reader, I have distinguished some passages which may be skipped without compromising the narrative, but which do provide essential background details.

Besides social organization and courtship, there are many other interesting aspects of Ruff biology. They moult, migrate, feed, breed and care for their offspring. All these properties have been the subject of various studies. They all seem to have connections with the Ruff's social system, and thus need to be included in this book.

I do not want to treat all these different features as separate items. In the earlier chapters I will try to integrate the various characteristics of the Ruff. In the last chapter I shall use that information again in combination with data from related species in order to conclude with some speculations about the descent of the Ruff and the evolution of its behaviour.

CHAPTER 2

The pugnacious father

In 1758 Linnaeus tried, in the tenth edition of his *Systema naturae*, to classify the various species of birds known to him. Almost all waders were placed in three main genera, *Charadrius*, *Scolopax* and *Tringa*. Only the Oystercatcher *Haematopus* and the Avocet *Recurvirostra* fell outside these groups. Most plovers and the Black-winged Stilt received the name *Charadrius*; all snipes, the Curlew, Whimbrel, godwits, redshanks and the Greenshank got the name *Scolopax*; and all other sandpipers, stints, lapwings, phalaropes and the Turnstone were named *Tringa*.

The Ruff received the name *Tringa pugnax*. The genus name *Tringa* was borrowed from Aristotle, while the species name *pugnax* is Latin for pugnacious. So, the Ruff's name became one of the first scientific bird names which referred to the behaviour of the species. Soon after Linnaeus, several naturalists

8

realized that various species within this genus differed so much from one another that they had to be classified in different genera. They all agreed that the Ruff deserved a separate genus name, but, initially, could not agree on what it should be. The name *Philomachus* (Greek for 'lover of a duel') had already been given in 1804 by B. Merrem, but it was to be more than a hundred years until this name was generally accepted. In 1816 a new genus name for the Ruff was introduced by Leach: *Pavoncella*, which was derived from the Latin word for decoration, but which was also identical to the Italian word for Lapwing, and was thus somewhat confusing. Another genus name for the Ruff, *Machetes* (Greek for 'combatant'), was introduced in 1817 by Cuvier. During the rest of the nineteenth century and at the beginning of the twentieth century the genus name *Machetes* was most often used, but a few authors (among them the famous ornithologist Hermann Schlegel) continued to use *Tringa*, and a few others reintroduced *Pavoncella*.

2.1 THE LEK SITE

The first time I was able to observe Ruffs at close range was in 1964 in the breeding sanctuary for meadow birds near Roderwolde, the same place where I started my study. I had to reach these meadows by bicycle from my home in Groningen. It was on an afternoon in the second half of April with reasonable weather. Only the wind was somewhat troublesome; I had to cycle against it in a flat landscape devoid of trees. After about an hour I reached the gate that I had to enter. The schoolteacher had told me that the mating ground of the Ruffs could not be seen from the road and that it would take about a quarter of an hour to walk to the lek site. During my walk I repeatedly looked for the birds through my binoculars. After some time I suddenly detected a number of fluttering wings, and gradually it became clear that these were the Ruffs I had hoped to see. About 100 m from them I stopped to see what was happening. The birds first looked around with long necks and flattened ruffs, but after a few minutes they resumed threatening, fighting and other display behaviour. Ten birds were present. They were the shape of Redshanks, although they were slightly larger, and had plumage which looked scaly. There were only males: they all possessed a ruff of feathers around the neck and tufts on the head, in various colours and patterns. In some of the birds this plumage was not yet fully developed. All ten were sitting close together beside the water on an area of less than 10 m diameter. I was immediately struck by the high degree of synchrony between the different individuals. Sometimes they all remained quiet, and then, suddenly, they would all start to move: to flutter their wings, to thrust their bills in one another's direction or to attack their companions. There could be real explosions of activity, but strangely enough it remained almost completely silent. One could only hear the sound of fast-moving feathers through the air and of striking bodies. The fights lasted only a few seconds, and then suddenly the birds were all quiet again, leaving some of the males standing, while others lay flat on the ground.

In spite of the synchrony in activity among them, I did not get the impression of looking at a group of members of a particular species. It was as if I had watched a stage play with highly individualistic actors. The differences in plumage between them dominated the whole scene. Looking at birds as individuals was a completely new bird-watching experience for me. Up to that moment I had been satisfied when I was able to establish the species name of the bird I had seen, or when I could give a precise estimate of the number of members of a particular species in a group or in a certain area. Now I could establish the presence of:

- an individual with a brown ruff and head-tufts and with black transverse banding;
- one with a black ruff and head-tufts and with fine white transverse stripes;
- one with a brown ruff and head-tufts and a white bib;
- one with a white ruff and black head-tufts;
- one with a completely white ruff and head-tufts.

There were also five other individuals, again with unique plumage characteristics.

This experience of being involved with individuals was crucial for my further scientific outlook. I realized that the differences between individual Ruffs were obvious to the observer, yet I was also aware that these differences did not evolve just for my convenience. Maybe they were important for intraspecific communication, and for the recognition of specific individuals. I suddenly realized that recognition of conspecific individuals could also be important in other species, even those without such obvious individual variation as the Ruff. This led me to a completely new perception and field of enquiry.

After a period of quietly watching from a long distance, I wanted to move a bit closer to prepare things for a more permanent watch, with the hope of taking photographs. When I started walking in the direction of the lek site, the birds all flew up. I stopped and a few minutes later they returned to the same site. They first showed erect postures with long necks and flattened ruffs, but soon they started to display their normal behaviour. I was still too far from the lek to set up my observation tent, so I started to walk again. When the birds took off, I continued to within about 30 m of the lek site. There, my tent was set up and my first study in animal behaviour began.

The leks near Roderwolde

An important property of a lek is its fixed location: a small piece of land which is used by a group of Ruffs for courtship and mating during the nesting season, mostly year after year. According to the local farmers, the lek near Roderwolde had been there for several tens of years. In fact, they were talking about two leks

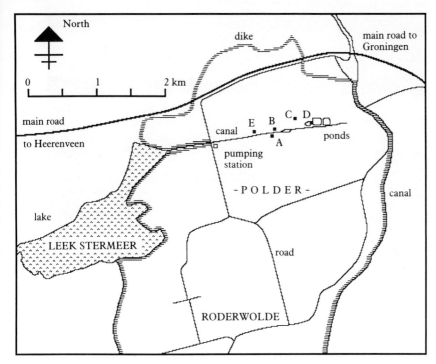

FIGURE 1 *Map of the study area near Roderwolde.*
A–E are the locations of the leks.

on both sides of the water. I stayed for nine seasons from 1964 to 1972 and found, within an area of about 4 km^2, no fewer than five places where Ruffs courted for several weeks in succession (Figure 1). All the sites were used for at least two years, but the extent to which they were exploited differed. One of them was the lek I observed during my first field season in 1964 (lek A). It was located at the border of an old canal in a marshy meadow. It was intensively used by the Ruffs during four successive seasons. The birds did not seem to be shy, and could often be approached to within 20 m. Sometimes more than 15 males were present, but at the start of the fifth season (1968) the lek was only occasionally visited by a few males. Later on that season it was completely abandoned. Three years later in 1971, however, a new lek with 4–10 males was established at the same place. It was maintained in the following season.

In my first field season there was also another lek (B) on the other side of the canal on a slight elevation in another marshy meadow. The distance between both leks was about 50 m. I did not observe lek B during the first two years, but I could see that it was very intensively used by the Ruffs. Again, the birds on this site paid hardly any attention to the presence of humans. The lek was main-

Overview of lek B near Roderwolde in 1968.

tained for seven successive seasons. In the middle of the seventh season four of the males were killed by a cat. At the start of the eighth season the lek was only occasionally visited by a few males and was abandoned later on.

In 1967 I discovered a third place (lek C) with a large number of displaying males. It was in the middle of a very wet meadow, partly inundated with a few centimetres of water, about 500 m east of the other two leks. Sometimes there were more than 50 males at this site, but the birds were shy and I was unable to approach them very closely. As soon as I came within 200 m, they flew up and did not return, but instead started to display in other meadows. For that reason I did not try to erect an observation tent. Lek C was also visited by many males the next year (1968), but in 1969 and in later seasons it was only occasionally visited by a few Ruffs.

In 1968 I carefully explored the surroundings of my study area with a small rowing-boat, and again I found two new leks. The first one (lek D) was about 1 km to the east. In fact, lek C was just half-way between lek D and leks A and B. The new lek was located on the muddy shore of a small pond. The birds on this site had an unobstructed view to the east over the water. To the west, however, they could not see anything because of a dense patch of reed. The birds were very tame and I was able to observe their behaviour from a distance of 50 m without using a hide. In the following three years lek D was frequently observed. It was visited by 10–20 males. In 1971 I built a tower from which lek D could be observed in detail, and leks A, B and C could be spotted with a telescope. I was curious as to whether the birds which were visiting lek D were also going to other leks in the neighbourhood. Unfortunately, activity on lek D decreased during that season. In my last observation season, 1972, lek D was only occasionally visited by a few males.

In 1968 I also found a very small group of males (lek E) about 500 m west of lek A and B. It occupied a slight elevation on the corner of the canal and a ditch and was visited by between two and six males who appeared to be less shy than those on lek C. They all returned after I placed a tent to watch their behaviour. In the next year I observed displaying males at the same site, but in the following years never saw them again.

Attachment to the lek site

My data from Roderwolde do not clearly support the idea that leks are visited for several tens of years, maybe even for centuries. None of the leks I observed was maintained during the whole study period of nine seasons. Lek A was abandoned during three seasons, lek B was left by the birds after seven seasons, and lek D also disappeared after four years of observations. It is possible that this decline of activity on the leks was caused by my disturbance. For instance, during the season that lek A was abandoned I was sleeping and living in a tent at the same side of the canal, only 80 m away. The following season, when no birds returned to lek A, I was living in a caravan at the same site. Similarly, the decline in the number of males on lek D might have been caused by the presence of my observation tower close by. The disappearance of lek B in 1971 was probably not because of my disturbance in that year, but could have been a consequence of the predatory visits of the cat in 1970. Another factor which may have caused lek desertion was the rapid change in agricultural methods over the period during which I collected my field data. This resulted in a considerable loss of suitable foraging areas for the species and of appropriate breeding habitats for reeves, and thus in a rapid decline of the population.

The males on one of the leks in Roderwolde did not show very strong site attachment (lek C). They flew up at the slightest sign of disturbance and frequently moved as a group to another part of the area to resume courtship. One might therefore question whether this community of Ruffs should still be considered a lek. It seemed to be an intermediate stage between a real lek, such as the leks A, B and D in Roderwolde, and a group of Ruffs with no site attachment at all. Courtship takes place in all kinds of groups, and, while a good deal can be observed on the leks, it may also occur in groups which are not confined to a particular place. Ruffs can usually be observed in company with other members of their species. They mostly migrate in groups, interrupt migration for feeding, moult together with many conspecifics, and may winter in enormous concentrations. Only the reeves perform some activities in isolation: namely laying and incubation. In groups of Ruffs, usually one sex predominates, and quite often the other sex is absent. Even in pure male groups which interrupt spring migration to stop over at a favourable foraging area, one may observe fighting, threat and behaviour patterns strongly reminiscent of male–female interactions on a lek. In particular the males with underdeveloped plumage are treated as if they were females. During spring I have seen many wandering groups of Ruffs in which foraging and resting behaviour was interspersed with courtship and fighting. I have observed many such groups in the neighbourhood of real leks, but also in other places offering good feeding or resting habitats.

On a few occasions male Ruffs did not court in groups, but alone, quite often on a fixed site. Usually they were only a few dozen metres away from other displaying ruffs, who could be alone, but who could also be in a group on a lek. Single males were sometimes visited by females. Although it was difficult to observe these single males accurately, I had the impression that they tended to follow the females more often than did the males on leks. Sometimes they visited the leks in their neighbourhood when females landed on these leks. Thus, display by singletons might be a consequence of a tendency of females not to visit the lek very often, but to pay many visits to its close surroundings. Single males may establish new leks. Consequently, the clustering of leks might be due to a tendency of single males not to stray very far from other ruffs.

Clustering of leks

All the leks I found were in the close vicinity of other leks and in most cases the distance to the nearest lek was less than 1 km. In a few cases leks were very close together; for instance, leks A and B in Roderwolde were only 50 m apart. Clustering of leks may be the result of the presence of suitable feeding areas for flocks of passing Ruffs, especially females. Almost all leks known to me were in the neighbourhood of shallow water or areas with mud, which were frequently visited by large flocks of foraging ruffs and reeves. For instance, the canal separating leks A and B contained about 50 cm of water and had a bed of soft mud at least 1 m deep. About 1 km from the leks the canal was separated from an area of higher water level by a dyke and a pumping station. In spring, before the cattle were left in the meadows, this polder was dried by pumping the water out of the canal. The capacity of the station was large enough to remove almost all the water from the canal in the course of an afternoon. It sometimes caused me problems when returning home, when I had gone to my observation tent by rowing across the canal. On one occasion it took me more than 30 minutes to reach the other side by ploughing with the oars through the mud. The empty canal was also an excellent feeding area for Ruffs, and I sometimes observed flocks of over 200 females probing with their bills in the soft mud.

I doubt, however, whether clustering of leks is due to ecological conditions alone. Close to Roderwolde I found several extensive areas which seemed to be suitable for leks, but which did not support any. In other districts I also saw large areas without leks which at first glance seemed highly suitable for them. These observations strongly suggest that the distribution of leks also depends on social interactions between leks.

Other leks

Roderwolde was not the only place where I observed Ruffs. In spring 1969 I explored a larger area, yielding four other leks which were thoroughly studied during two successive years, 1970 and 1971. Two of them, namely those near Boerakker and Sebaldeburen (Figure 2), were located on top of a canal dyke. The 10–20 males on these leks formed a line, so they had an unobstructed view in all directions and were not easily disturbed by an observer or a tent. The third lek near Terwispel was extremely large. It was situated in a marshy meadow bordering the former course of a small river. Sometimes the lek was visited by more than 50 males. Although this was almost as many as the highest number observed on lek C in Roderwolde, there were enormous differences between these two leks. The birds on the lek near Terwispel were very tame: quite often I was able to approach to as close as 15 m of the lek and to enter my tent without any birds leaving. They were very strongly attached to that particular site, and when they were displaced by human activity they returned as soon as possible. The soil of the lek area was trampled almost bare by the continuous presence of a large number of Ruffs. I never saw these birds displaying in groups in neighbouring meadows. The fourth lek near Gorredijk was fairly close to the third one, but much smaller. It differed from all other leks I studied by the absence of water nearby. This lek was located at the edge of an asphalt road and could be observed from a car parked 10 m away.

Observing leks

Almost all leks were studied from observation tents of 1 m^3, placed 15–30 m away for several days or weeks at a time. To obtain permission to erect these tents I had to visit many farmers, all cattle breeders. They were hard-working people, starting work as early as 4 a.m. to milk their cows. I mostly visited them around noon, because they were usually at home then. When I arrived just after their meal, I sometimes disturbed the whole family during the midday siesta: all the family members were sitting around the table next to their empty dishes, sleeping with their heads in their hands, their elbows on the table. Most farmers were helpful and greatly interested in the work I was doing. They knew a lot about the birds and were able to give me a great deal of information about Ruffs and the area in general.

I once asked a farmer whether it was possible to place my sleeping tent on his field. He had no objections. The field would first be used for hay, and his cattle would not be put into it before the middle of June. A week later, however, he asked whether I minded if he changed his plans. He wanted to bring his cows to that particular meadow within a few days, but of course he did not object to the presence of my tent. To accommodate it, he would make a fence to leave a strip of land of at least 10 m wide and 50 m long. This he did. My relations with the local people could not have been better!

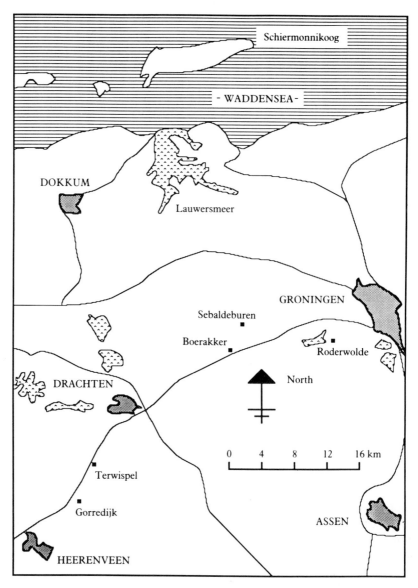

FIGURE 2 *The leks studied in the northern part of the Netherlands.*

Some of my tents were placed on platforms, such that a floor was created, 1 m high. All the tents were easy to erect and very stable, but during a very heavy storm at the end of April 1970 two tents collapsed. My own tent was rescued in tatters after six years of faithful service. The second one had completely disappeared from its place on a dyke when I arrived after the storm. The storm was blowing towards the water, so I presumed the tent to have been blown into the canal. Borrowing a rowing boat from a farmer, I tried to discover my tent by carefully probing the water with the oars. Suddenly I saw a very small end of an iron pole sticking out above the surface. I approached it and pulled. Indeed, it was the tent, almost undamaged, but completely submerged. After retrieving it, I erected it again on the dyke and continued my observations on the following day.

About half my observations were started in the early morning, between 30 minutes and one hour before sunrise. When I was living in Groningen I had to get up about two hours earlier. Especially later on in the season, it became very hard to leave my bed at the right time, and five early-morning observations per week was the absolute maximum possible. I was unable to adapt my internal rhythm exclusively to fieldwork on Ruffs. I wanted to do other things and to see other people, but most of these activities were only possible during the evenings. Early-morning observations were continued for three to four hours. On most occasions the Ruffs were already present when I arrived. My other observations were mainly in the afternoon, though some were during the rest of the day. Usually they did not last as long as my morning observations, being two to three hours in duration.

Early in spring it could be very cold in the small tent, and this did not permit much movement. Sometimes the tent was frozen, and I had to unfreeze the zip with my bare hands before I could enter. On a few occasions I had to break the ice on the canal with the oars before I could reach the other side with the rowing boat. However, frost was not the worst of it. Strong winds or a storm on the front of my hide were even worse. I had to wear many, many layers of clothes, and to keep my feet warm I used wooden clogs. To remain warm during the whole observation session and to keep awake I had a second breakfast in the tent with large helpings of hot coffee from a thermos flask. This considerable volume of liquid created new physiological problems which could hardly be solved within my small living area! Later in the season it could become very hot in the small tent, especially when there was no wind and the sun was beating on the roof. On clear mornings in early May I would enter the tent when it was still freezing, but could be forced to leave at 9.00 because of the blazing sun, even after undressing inside.

Subsequent investigations

After completing my thesis in 1973 I did not continue fieldwork on the Ruff. On a few occasions, however, I had the opportunity to watch Ruffs on their leks. In 1975 I came into contact with an American, Julia Shepard, who wanted to come to the Netherlands to photograph and film Ruffs on a large lek. I phoned the warden of the sanctuary in which the lek near Terwispel was located, to ask whether she and her field assistant could get permission to work on one or more leks in his neighbourhood and whether they could live somewhere nearby during the field season. Both permission and accommodation were arranged. In the beginning of April they arrived in Groningen, and I took them to the area. They worked on two leks: the large one near Terwispel, and a smaller one in the same neighbourhood which I had not previously discovered but which compared favourably with the other lek sites. Both Americans had a great time and filmed successfully. I went to see them in the middle of the season and paid short visits to the leks. It gave me a feeling of nostalgia: perhaps I could resume my work on the Ruffs in the future.

In 1975 I also came into contact with a student from Amsterdam, Joop Brinkkemper, who was studying the Ruffs in his neighbourhood. He wanted to include this work in his degree studies, just as I did, but could not get any guidance in the University of Amsterdam. I was asked to help him a bit, and was happy to do so. During an extensive correspondence and several visits I got the opportunity to see his leks near Zaandam, north of Amsterdam. These leks were also situated in wet, rather saline meadows, bordering ditches and canals.

From 1977 to 1979 I was studying the behaviour of Black-headed Gulls at their breeding colonies in the Lauwersmeer, a former part of the Waddensea, enclosed in 1969. Here I also observed a large number of Ruffs, sometimes roving in flocks from one area to another, sometimes displaying on leks which seemed to be attached to particular locations. The number of breeding reeves seemed to be high in this area. My spare hours were spent looking for Ruffs and observing some of their leks from a hide. The parts of the Lauwersmeer chosen by the Ruffs for their leks (and also by flocks for temporary display) were former sandbanks, especially the elevated parts without high vegetation. The soil was still salty, the vegetation very low and sparse. Most leks were visited by 5–20 males. In contrast to my earlier experience, many of these leks were not at the edge of open water. Nevertheless, the birds had an almost unobstructed view in all directions.

Leks in other studies

The tendency of Ruffs to court on leks is not exclusively a Dutch habit. It has been reported from almost all countries where Ruffs are known to breed (Figure 3). The leks on Tipperne in Denmark, were, according to Andersen and Bancke and Meesenburg, located in a cluster on elevated parts (hills) of a former salt marsh. The presence of water was not essential in the immediate vicinity of the leks. They were visited by 5–15 males, and thus the situation was very similar to that in the Lauwersmeer. In OstFriesland, West Germany, the leks are, according to Siedel, also clustered and in many cases at the edge of water on dykes or other elevated areas. In the same region Mildenberger observed several males displaying alone, each 400–700 m apart. On the islands Oie and Kirr in northern East Germany, the situation seems, according to Spillner and

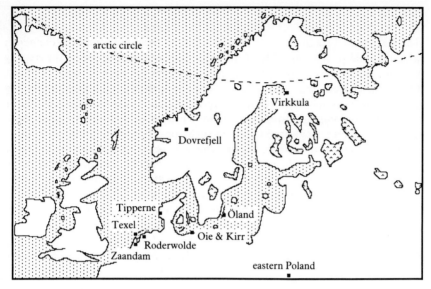

FIGURE 3 *The leks studied by various other investigators.*

Scheufler and Stiefel, very similar to that on Tipperne. In Eastern Poland in the 1930s Lindemann observed four clustered leks visited by several dozens of males, with distances between nearest leks of about 500 m. They were located in a wet meadow on slight elevations. Ruffs have also been seen displaying on leks in Scandinavia. In Dovrefjell in Norway the leks may, according to Kvaerne, consist of a group of hummocks which rise just above the water resulting from melted snow. On Öland in Sweden Shepard observed leks which were visited by about 10 males and were located near the water on slight moorland elevations. The three leks studied by Lank and Smith at Virkkula near the northern Baltic coast of Finland was visited by less than 10 males each, and were not very stable. They were located on raised areas in a marshy region and were only 50–200 m apart. A comparison between the Dutch and Scandinavian findings might suggest that very large leks only occur in the south of the breeding range. However, observations by Kistchinskij and Flint and by Tomkovich of leks with about 50 males in the delta of the Indigirka River (northeastern Yakutia) show that this is not always so. Recent observations by Khlebosolov (close to the Konkovaya River in the same region) confirm that large leks may be formed there (but also small ones) and further show that the males are not strongly attached to their communal display grounds and spend considerable time on personal display sites away from the leks.

Summary

The lek site is a small piece of land, usually an area of about 10 m diameter, which is used by a group of Ruffs for courtship and mating during the nesting season, mostly year after year. It may be used for several tens of years. Courtship of Ruffs may also occur outside the traditional lek sites in foraging groups, but probably less frequently and less completely than on leks. Ruffs displaying in foraging groups are more sensitive to disturbance than those displaying on leks. Leks are located on slight elevations or on other sites, quite often close to the water, where the birds have an unobstructed view in several or all directions. Leks may be visited by a few, occasionally one, or up to about 50 males at the same time. Leks often occur in clusters. Leks may be as little as 50 m, but usually several hundreds of metres or more, apart. Clusters of leks are further away from one another: several kilometres or more. The areas in which leks are found are usually wet with short and sparse vegetation: moorland, tundra, salt marsh and damp meadow are favoured. These areas may become inundated during the winter or early spring. Some of them have salty soils.

2.2 Territories

All the leks which I could observe at close quarters were visited by several males. Some individuals were always seen at a specific site on the lek, only 30–60 cm in diameter. Such sites, or *residences*, were defended by the resident male against other territorial males. Males might continue to visit the same residence for weeks, spending up to 90% of the daylight hours on these residences, and a few even stayed overnight. As a result, many residences lost all vegetation in the course of the season, becoming mere patches of bare earth. Residences which were less frequently visited became visible as small areas of trampled grass with numerous dabs of white faeces. Some maps of typical leks are given in Figures 4, 5 and 6. Bare patches of earth are indicated by solid lines, and areas of trampled grass by broken lines. The numbers refer to territorial males on the different sites. The first example shows a small permanent lek with six resident males situated in line on top of a dyke near Boerakker during the 1972 season. The second one shows lek D in Roderwolde in 1970 with 11 resident males on temporary residences in a muddy area at the edge of a pond. In the periods when this area was flooded, the birds moved to the adjacent higher spots. The third example is a large permanent lek with 30 resident males near Terwispel, also during the 1970 season.

The distribution of residences among the resident males of a lek does not remain constant during the course of a season. To give an impression of the dynamics of territoriality in the Ruff, I shall describe my observations on lek B during the 1968 season. It refers to my most complete record of the events on one single lek. During that season my attention was almost entirely focussed on

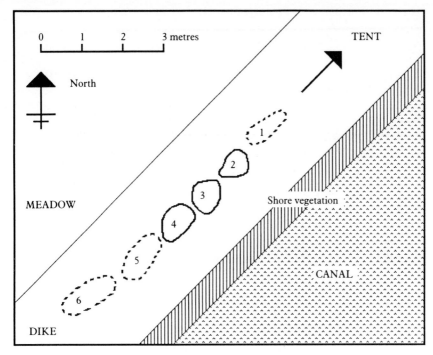

FIGURE 4 *Map of the lek near Boerakker, 12 May 1972.*
Patches with a closed outline are bare earth; patches with a broken outline are
trampled grass. Resident males are indicated by numbers.

that particular mating area and I was able to record most changes on the lek
immediately or within a few hours. My observations in other seasons and at
other leks show that this season at Roderwolde is representative of a typical lek.

The actors on the stage

At the outset, I must introduce the most important resident males, those who
stayed for at least 30 days on the lek. First I shall consider the situation on 7 May
1968. At 4.00 a.m. I was seated in my observation tent at the east side of the lek.
It was fairly windy, sometimes clear, sometimes cloudy with light rain, and not
very warm. I stayed until 7.00 a.m. at my post, observing a morning with
reasonable activity. The maximum number of males present together was 12,
and the maximum number of females was three. There were no real copulations.
I saw only one intention to crouch by a female, and two mounts by a male on
another male. During these three hours of observation I scored 41 aggressive
encounters between males, a reasonable number. These encounters were

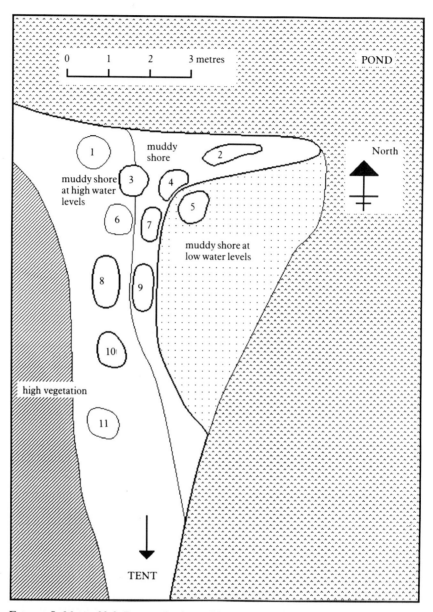

FIGURE 5 *Map of lek D near Roderwolde, 1 May 1970.*
Patches with a thick outline are bare earth; patches with a thin outline are trampled
vegetation. Resident males are indicated by numbers.

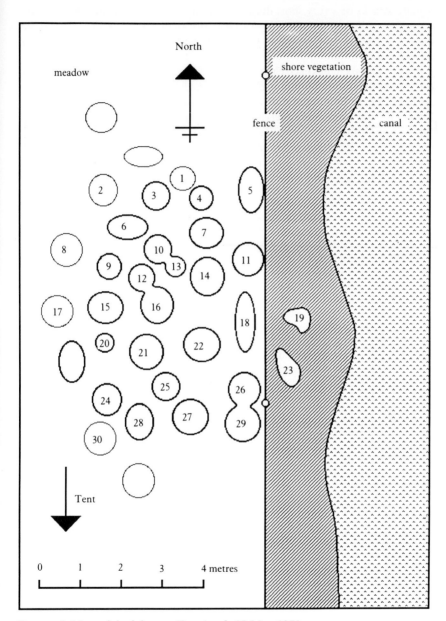

FIGURE 6 *Map of the lek near Terwispel, 15 May 1970.*
Patches with a thick outline are bare earth; patches with a thin outline are trampled
grass. Resident males are indicated by numbers.

usually attacks of a very short duration lasting only a few seconds. Perhaps the most interesting occurrence was an angry Moorhen who, at 5.35 a.m., ran like mad over the lek and chased all the ruffs to within a few metres of their usual quarters.

There were six males each clearly defending a residence, and each was present for at least 172 of the 180 minutes I watched the lek in total. A seventh male, who also seemed to be attached to a particular site, stayed for only 46 minutes. During the three hours of observation, the seven resident males spent altogether 1103 minutes on the lek. The sum duration of all visits by other males was 472 minutes, and 90 minutes for females. Fluctuations in the numbers of the different classes of individuals – resident males, satellites, marginal males, and females – are shown in Figure 7.

Figure 7 clearly demonstrates that, in contrast to the other classes, the basic level of lek attendance in resident males (Figure 7A) is high, and the periods with low visiting rates are short. The graph for satellite males (Figure 7B) reveals a low basic level of satellite visits, alternating with relatively short peaks of high visiting rates. The basic rate of visiting by marginal males (Figure 7C) is lower than for satellites. The distribution of visits by marginal males shows short high peaks which strongly resemble the distribution of satellite visits. The females (Figure 7D) visited the lek during six sessions, lasting 3–37 minutes. Most of these sessions coincided with high visiting rates of the other categories. The number of resident males during the sessions was high (six or seven), except during the fifth one, when the approaching female was probably not noticed by the resident males, who foraged in the neighbourhood. The number of satellite males was also high during these sessions, especially during the longest one. The number of marginal males showed a similar trend and reached its maximum around the beginning of the long session of female attendance.

To recognize the males I mainly used colours and patterns in their ruffs and head-tufts, and the colours of the wattles on the forepart of the head between bill and eyes (Figure 8). Additionally, many birds were trapped in the course of my study and were given colour rings for unambiguous identification. Ruffs and head-tufts could be black, grey, white and different shades of brown: beige, yellowish, light brown, reddish, orange or dark brown. They could be plain or mixed with other colours in a regular or an irregular pattern: narrow or broad transverse striping, small or large irregular patches or dashes, and zones of different colours under the chin, resembling a child's bib, or a multi-coloured fan. The wattles could be yellow, orange or red.

All seven males had black in their ruffs but in only one was it plain black. His head-tufts were reddish brown and the wattles around the base of his bill were yellow. He occupied a place at the west side of the lek (Figure 9), far away from my observation site. He was rarely involved in aggressive encounters: only four times during my observation session of three hours and as equally often as an attacker as the victim of an attack. This male appeared to be most successful on lek B in 1968, although he was a newcomer on that lek. He got 45 copulations out of an observed total of 101 in 1968. In the two preceding seasons he visited lek A, but not as a faithful resident male. He will be called *Boss* in the rest of this book and indicated by an *asterisk* in the figures.

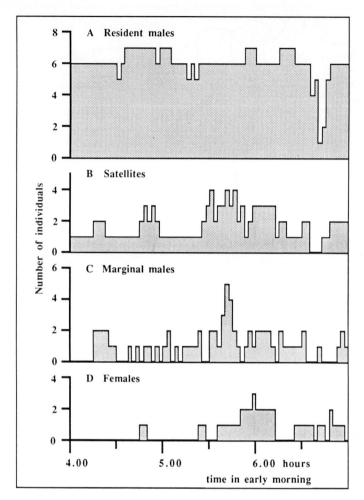

FIGURE 7 *Numbers of resident males (A), satellites (B), marginal males (C), and females (D) on lek B near Roderwolde, 7 May 1968, 4.00–7.00 a.m.*

A second male looked rather similar. His black ruff, however, had a large white patch, and his head-tufts were light brown with tiny black spots. His wattles were also yellow. He occupied a position at the border of the water, at the southern edge of the lek, somewhat lower than the other residences. He engaged in aggressive encounters about as often as most other males that morning, but mostly as the victim of an attack. This male was less successful than Boss in the 1968 season. He got only five of the copulations I observed, but in the season before (1967) he was the most successful male on lek B. In 1966 I also observed him as a resident male on the same lek. I do not know

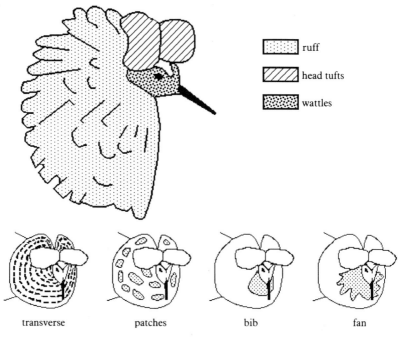

FIGURE 8 *The nuptial plumage of males and the various patterns in their ruffs.*

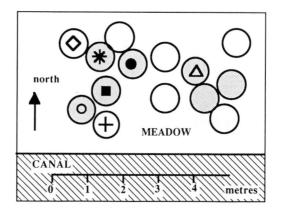

FIGURE 9 *Map of lek B near Roderwolde, 7 May 1968. The position of the observation tent is about 15 m eastward. Filled circles are patches of bare earth; open circles are patches of trampled grass. Resident males are indicated by symbols: Boss, asterisk; Grandpa, plus; Yellow-face, black square; Orange-face, black circle; Fireman, open circle; Bib, open triangle; Fan-male, open diamond.*

whether he was very old, but in view of his decreasing success he will be called *Grandpa* and indicated by a *plus* in the figures.

There were two males with black ruffs with a fine light brown transverse striping and plain black head-tufts. The wattles of one were yellow. This male had a position between Boss and Grandpa, in the middle of the lek. He took part, primarily as an attacker, in many more aggressive encounters than did the other males that morning. I observed nine copulations by him in 1968. The wattles of the other one, who was situated at the east side of Boss, were orange. He had as many aggressive encounters as most other males on May 7, mostly as an attacker. He was seen to copulate only twice in 1968. Both males defended a residence on the same lek in the year before and probably also in 1966. The first one, called *Yellow-face*, will be indicated by a *black square* in the figures, and the other one, *Orange-face*, by a *black circle*.

There was a male with a black ruff with orange in a fan-like pattern, red head-tufts and red wattles. His position was south of Boss, just at the west side of Yellow-face and Grandpa. He had as many aggressive encounters as most other males, both as an attacker and as the victim of an attack. He was an important resident male on the same lek in 1966 and in 1967. In 1968 he was seen to copulate 12 times. This fifth male will be called *Fireman*, because of his red head, and will be indicated by an *open circle* in the figures.

The sixth male had a reddish brown ruff with white in a bib-like pattern and a few black patches. He had head-tufts of the same reddish-brown colour as his ruff and possessed yellow wattles. His position was at the east side of the lek, rather close to my observation tent. This male engaged in aggressive encounters as often as most other males. In 1967 and in 1966 he also defended a residence on the same lek, but in none of the seasons did I see him copulate. He will be called *Bib*, and indicated in the figures by an *open triangle*.

The male who was not present so much on 7 May had a black ruff with orange in a conspicuous fan-like pattern and with a few white patches. He further possessed orange head-tufts with tiny black spots and red wattles. He occupied a position behind Boss at the extreme west of the lek, as seen from my observation tent. Considering the fact that this male spent only a small amount of time on the lek, he was engaged in aggressive encounters as much as most other males, but only as the victim of an attack. This male was also an old friend. He defended a residence on the same lek in 1966 and 1967. In 1968 he was seen to copulate three times. This seventh male will be called *Fan-male*, and indicated in the figures with an *open diamond*.

In the spring of 1968 I observed 14 other males who defended a residence on lek B for one or a few days. Plumage details for these, as well as for the seven males introduced on page 24, are summarized in Table 1. In the following paragraphs I want to review the behaviour of these males on lek B during the 1968 season. A summary of the main facts on all 21 resident males during 1968 is given in Table 2.

One season on lek B

My observations in 1968 started around the middle of March. On 23 March I was able to identify the first Ruff of that season: Fireman was foraging with four

Table 1 Lek B, Roderwolde 1968: description of resident males.

Name of male	Ruff	Head-tufts	Wattles	Rings
Boss	bl	br	y	w
Grandpa	bl (PT w)	l-br tr bl	y	y
Yellow-face	bl tr l-br	bl	y	w
Orange-face	bl tr l-br	bl	o	g
Fireman	bl F o	r	r	b
Bib	r-br B w (PT bl)	r-br	y	y
Fan-male	bl F o (PT w)	o (pt bl)	r	w
1	br TR bl	br TR bl	y	y
2	s-bl tr l-br	s-bl	y	—
3	bl pt br	bl	o-y	—
4	bl tr br	bl tr br	o-y	—
5	bl tr be	be	o-y	—
6	bl tr l-br	bl	o	—
7	bl (PT w)	w F bl	y	w
8	bl tr lb	bl	y	r
9	w (PT bl)	r-br	o-y	w
10	w b bl (F bl)	l-br tr bl	y	y
11	bl tr be	bl	y	b
12	w TR bl	w	r	w
13	bl PT w + br	br	o-y	w
14	r-br	bl	r	w

Key: first basic colour, then pattern and colour of pattern; bl, black; gy, grey; w, white; l, light; d, dark; s, shining; y, yellow; g, green; b, blue; r, red; o, orange; be, beige; br, brown; tr, transverse striping; pt, patches; b, bib; f, fan; capitals, coarse pattern; small type, fine pattern; (—), few.

unknown males in the neighbourhood of lek A. The first visits to lek B were recorded on the morning of 27 March: groups of 20–50 individuals, perhaps with a few females, were foraging close to the lek. A few males, among them Fireman and Yellow-face, paid short visits to the lek, but did not show any signs of attachment to particular sites within it. On 30 March I discovered Bib for the first time in the neighbourhood of lek A.

During many of my visits to Roderwolde at the end of March and the beginning of April I saw big flocks of Ruffs, all or almost all males, foraging at different sites in the polder area, and occasionally in the neighbourhood of the leks. When such a group was close to a lek, a few males left the group, flew to the lek, started to display there, and sometimes had short disputes with one another. Such visits rarely lasted longer than a few minutes.

On 7 April I discovered Boss on lek A for the first time. On 8 April Fan-male was seen for the first time, also on lek A. Lek B was not visited very often during these observations. On 12 April lek B became more attractive, perhaps because it was visited by several females. Bib, Yellow-face, Orange-face, Fireman and

Table 2 Lek B, Roderwolde 1968: main statistics of the resident males.

Name of male	Number of days on residence	Total number of copulations	Mean number of agonistic encounters/h	Attacks as a percentage of all encounters
Boss	54	45	1.2	77
Grandpa	39	5	2.5	52
Yellow-face	49	9	3.2	78
Orange-face	32	2	1.8	70
Fireman	54	14	1.5	39
Bib	38	0	1.8	47
Fan-male	35	3	1.8	41
1	5	2	3.3	23
2	3	1	3.8	67
3	4	0	0.5	50
4	5	0	2.9	46
5	5	0	0.8	0
6	1	0	—	—
7	1	1	3.6	67
8	3	0	2.3	14
9	2	0	—	—
10	1	0	10.0	20
11	9	1	2.7	60
12	9	1	2.1	38
13	12	1	1.3	64
14	4	0	0.3	0

Fan-male came to lek B, but still lek A was visited by many more individuals, for example by Boss. It was not until 15 April that one of the males on lek B developed a clear attachment to a particular site. It was Bib. Later in the season I could see that his preferred site was, strangely enough, closer to my observation tent than all the other residences which were established. Perhaps the other males were afraid of my tent. Although Bib was the only male with a distinct residence on 15 April, lek B was visited by four other males, who spent as much time there as Bib: Yellow-face, Orange-face, Fireman and Fan-male.

The situation remained unchanged until 18 April. Lek B was visited by many ruffs, and also by reeves, but none of the other males became attached to a particular territory. On a few occasions Boss also visited lek B, for instance on 18 April, around 5.30. That same morning around 7.20 a large number of ruffs and two reeves landed on lek A, and lek B was abandoned as all the males joined the party on lek A. There was a lot of activity, culminating at 7.43 with a copulation by Boss, the first copulation I saw that season. I left the observation tent at 8.45 and returned the same day at 16.45. To my great surprise Boss was no longer present on lek A but had moved to lek B and had established his own residence.

In view of that first copulation, I had expected him to occupy a territory on lek A. I do not know what happened between 8.45 and 16.45, but I suspect that several females landed on lek B, that all males from lek A joined this group, and that Boss got another couple of copulations on lek B. During the time Boss was establishing a territory about 5 m west of Bib, Fireman and Orange-face occupied territories between Bib and Boss. Thus, in the late afternoon of 18 April four males were situated in line, from west to east: Boss, Fireman, Orange-face and Bib.

It would be impractical to describe all the subsequent events on the lek in the same detail, the more so as all changes are summarized in a long series of diagrams in Figure 10. I only want to review some major changes in residence occupation, and the events which possibly caused these changes.

After Boss established on lek B, the number of resident males gradually grew to 13 on 23 April. During this phase I observed many copulations, especially by Boss, Yellow-face and some satellite males. In the very early morning of 24 April I placed mist-nets close to lek B, just behind a strip of reed. I knew that most males and females arriving on the lek skimmed these reeds when landing. Because many Ruffs had visited the lek during the previous days, and because the weather conditions were excellent (a bit misty), I expected to catch lots of males and females for ringing. However, it turned into a real disaster! The birds which did come back to the lek swerved like acrobats over the net, but many did not come back at all. I could not catch a single ruff or reeve, and the number of resident males declined suddenly from 13 to 6! Only Boss, Fireman, Yellow-face, Orange-face, Fan-male and male 1 (with a reddish brown ruff with broad black transverse stripes and similar head-tufts) stayed on their residences. Realizing that my activities could have caused this sudden decline, I never again tried to catch Ruffs with mist-nets on the lek.

During the three weeks after my unsuccessful netting attempt the situation remained more or less stable with six or seven resident males, although they often changed position. The males became less active, received fewer females on the lek, and, especially towards the end of this period, were rarely seen to copulate. The first copulation, after an interval of 11 days of low activity, was on 13 May by Boss. From that time onwards events on the lek became more exciting again. On 14 May the lek was visited by females for long periods and I saw two copulations. This trend continued during the next few days. The number of resident males increased to nine on 16 May, but then suddenly decreased on 17 May. Again, this second decline could have been caused by my trapping activity, because I frequently tried to catch the males with snares on their residences. Trapped birds were described, measured, and marked with rings (a numbered aluminium one and a coloured plastic one) to facilitate identification. Especially when new males established on the lek, my trapping activity, and thus the extent of disturbance, increased. This was probably one of the reasons for continual fluctuations in the number of resident males until the beginning of June. There were many changes during this period, mainly as a result of the establishment of new males.

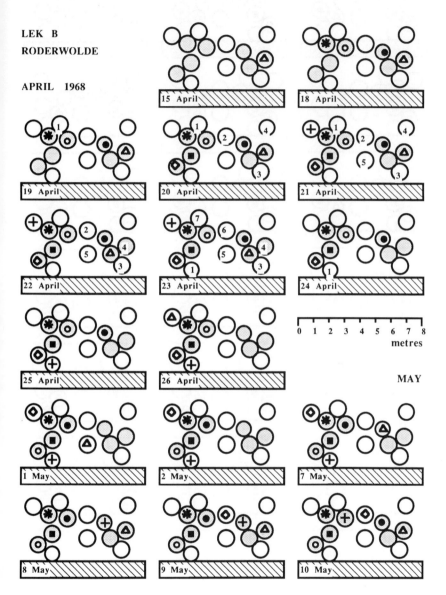

FIGURE 10 *The pattern of residence occupation on lek B near Roderwolde in 1968. Filled circles are patches of bare earth; open circles are patches of trampled grass. The main resident males are indicated by symbols, the other resident males by numbers. Meaning of symbols as in Figure 9.*

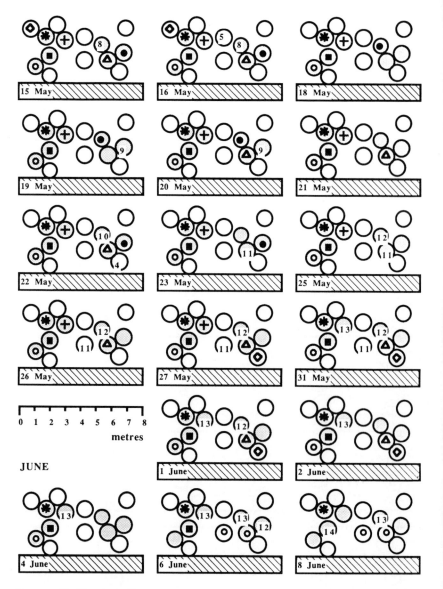

FIGURE 10 *Continued.*

Changes in residence possession

Some of the resident males maintained their territories for a considerable time. Boss displayed the strongest ties to his site on the lek. For almost two months he remained continuously at the same residence. Fireman stayed during the same period, but moved twice to another residence. Yellow-face's residence was somewhat shorter but also faithful to his initial territory. Many other resident males moved frequently, and were sometimes absent for a few days between periods of residency. For instance, Bib changed his position at least five times, and was absent altogether for about two weeks between the periods during which he defended a residence.

A few resident males lost their position because they were displaced by other males. For instance, Grandpa was repeatedly attacked by non-territorial males, and in the early morning of 23 May engaged in a very serious fight lasting four minutes, ultimately being able to retain his position. About one week later, however, on 31 May, he was forced to leave.

In the early morning a new male with a black ruff with irregular white and black patches and brown head-tufts (male 13) developed a preference for a residence north of male 12 and Grandpa. At 8.20, while Grandpa was briefly absent, male 13 moved onto Grandpa's residence. Grandpa returned one minute later and vigorously attacked male 13. Both males fought for three minutes and the encounter concluded with the departure of Grandpa. One hour later I tried to catch this new male, but unfortunately Grandpa returned and was re-trapped. Thereafter male 13 came back to the residence. I saw Grandpa returning in the afternoon at 16.13. Again he attacked male 13, but, after two minutes of fighting, made his final departure.

Many of the cases of residence desertion in 1968 on lek B seem to have been associated with disturbance, especially trapping, so perhaps the observed number of changes on the lek was much higher than under normal conditions. From my experiences on the same lek in the years when few or no birds were caught, and my observations on other leks, I believe that changes were not much more numerous, or at most only a little more so. I observed on all leks that the spatial distribution of resident males changed almost every day. Only a few males, like Boss, Yellow-face and Fireman in 1968 on lek B, stayed for weeks or even months on one and the same site. These were also the males most successful in copulating. On a few leks the spatial distribution of the males was associated with changing water level: the whole group would follow the altered shoreline. When the water level dropped, even successful males changed position so as to stay close to the water. Although they frequently changed position, successful males on these shoreline leks stayed on the lek continuously for about two months. However, on all leks that I observed, most territorial males defended the same residence for only a few days and stayed on the lek for one or a few weeks only.

In 1968 I only once saw a new male take a residence from an established resident male by means of a serious fight: the settlement of male 13 on 31 May at the expense of Grandpa. In 1969 I saw another take over on lek B with a lot of fighting. In that year male 1 settled again on lek B around the middle of April. He was rather active, but I did not see any copulations by this bird. After a period of about 10 days' defence of his residence he lost his position on the lek.

In the early morning of 27 April he arrived about a quarter of an hour later than most other resident males. In the meantime, Fireman, who also returned in 1969, enlarged his own territory with male 1's residence. When male 1 finally arrived on the lek at 4.59, he was chased away by Fireman. A few minutes later a new male with a white ruff and black head-tufts arrived at the border of the lek. This male, who will be called *Black & White* hereafter, was to stay on the lek for the next two weeks on male 1's residence. Meanwhile there was a lot of activity on the lek, with many females present and several copulations. At 5.13 male 1 returned again, flew to his residence, had a prolonged dispute with Fireman, and was able to chase Fireman from his residence. Thereafter, male 1 was attacked at least nine times during the next 30 minutes, mainly by Fireman, but also by other resident males. Male 1 attacked only twice in return during the same period. Nevertheless, male 1 got several females on his residence, but no copulations. At 6.18 several resident males, among them male 1, left the lek. At 6.20 Black & White occupied male 1's residence. At 6.24 Black & White was twice attacked by his neighbour, Bib, who also returned in 1969. Then, at 6.25, Black & White attacked Bib in return. During that fight male 1 came back to the lek and the fight between Bib and Black & White was followed by a long and arduous one between male 1 and Black & White. Thereafter, Black & White was attacked three times by Bib, and Black & White again had a long fight with male 1. At 6.27 Black & White was attacked three times by neighbouring males, but in return he attacked male 1, also three times. Then male 1 left his residence, Black & White stayed, and at 6.28 male 1 also left the lek. During the next 10 minutes Black & White was attacked five times by his neighbours, but remained firmly on his newly established residence and, in the end, became tolerated by his neighbours.

The establishment of a residence by means of a major dispute with the previous possessor seems to be a normal pattern, but is certainly not the commonest way that a resident male establishes himself. In most cases new males seem to settle on vacant residences at the border of a lek. They may gradually move to the centre if vacancies arise. In many cases this is accompanied by some fighting with prospective neighbours, but usually without major disputes.

Attachment to leks by the territory owners

For the defence of a residence, fighting plays a role, and threat behaviour towards neighbours seems to be important too. Presence on the residence, however, seems to be the most essential factor for maintaining it. The resident males of the same lek always keep an eye on their neighbours. Residents often leave the lek together for foraging, and also return as a group, but for the greatest part of the day (75–90%) all resident males stay on the lek. Figure 11 gives an example of the presence of resident males on lek B in Roderwolde during a period of low activity (18 May 1968, 14.00–16.00). All five resident males left the lek from 14.50 to 14.52 and from 15.49 to 15.51. In particular, the neighbours Boss and Grandpa (and to some extent Orange-face) showed closely related occupancies. The most central male, Yellow-face, was the one most often present on his residence. Fireman, who occupied a residence at the periphery, behaved independently of the others (see also Figure 10).

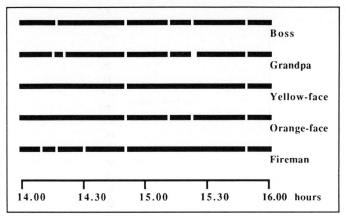

FIGURE 11   *The presence of five resident males on lek B near Roderwolde, 18 May 1968, 14.00–16.00.*

Resident males tend to spend the whole day on the lek, in contrast to the other classes of individuals, who show a clear preference for visiting the lek in the early morning and afternoon. The data collected in 1968 were not very useful for demonstrating this phenomenon because most observations were done early in the morning. In 1969 my observations were more equally spread over the day. Figure 12 gives an idea of the changes in visiting rates of resident males and the other classes of individuals and refers to all data collected on lek B in Roderwolde in the period 20–27 April 1969. The diagrams show the relationship between the average time of day of an observation session (most sessions lasted two to four hours) and the average visiting rate during that session.

Figure 12A shows the daily changes in the percentage time spent by resident males on the lek. They tend to be present for 80–100% of the time throughout the day. The highest visiting rates occur in the early morning, and (especially at the beginning and in the middle of the season) in the afternoon. The lowest visiting rates seem to occur between 8.00 and 12.00. Figures 12B, 12C and 12D show the daily fluctuations in the number of satellites, marginal males and females simultaneously present on the lek. Quite frequently the average number of individuals of these classes is much lower than 1. All the diagrams show roughly the same trends. Daily changes in female visiting rates (Figure 12D) closely resemble those in satellites (Figure 12B) and marginal males (Figure 12C).

Figure 13 gives an idea of the changes in visiting rates of resident males and the other classes during the season. It contains all data from continuous observation sessions from 15 minutes before sunrise to 75 minutes after sunrise collected on lek B in Roderwolde during the 1968 season. All the diagrams show the correlation between time of the season and visiting rate.

Figure 13A shows the seasonal changes in the average percentage of time spent by resident males on the lek. This value is fairly low, around 50%, at the start of the

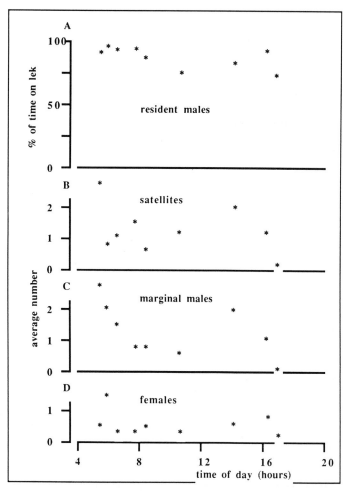

FIGURE 12 *The daily fluctuations in the average percentage of time spent by a resident male (A), and in the average numbers of satellites (B), marginal males (C), and females (D) on lek B near Roderwolde from 20 to 27 April 1969.*

season, but soon rises to a level fluctuating between 80% and 100%. Figures 13B, 13C, 13D and 13E show for the different classes the seasonal fluctuations in the average number of individuals simultaneously present on the lek. There is a certain degree of synchrony between the fluctuations of the different classes. The peaks in the average number of females present on the lek are around 22 April, 30 April, 17 May and 7 June. All peaks coincide with high levels of the average percentage of time spent by resident males on the lek. They are also associated with peaks in the average number of resident males and satellites on the lek. The similarity between the graphs for females and for marginal males is less strong. Peaks in the average number of marginal males on the lek

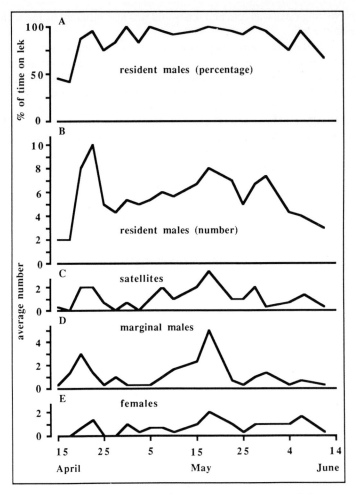

FIGURE 13 *The seasonal changes in the average percentage of time spent by a resident male (A) and change in the average numbers of resident males (B), satellites (C), marginal males (D), and females (E) on lek B near Roderwolde in 1968.*

seem to precede peaks in the average number of females, except for the highest peaks in both graphs, which occurred at the same time.

Similar fluctuations occur in any season, but the timing of peaks and periods with low visiting rates differs between seasons. The precise timing seems to depend on external factors, such as weather, foraging opportunities, activity of predators, and disturbance by humans. The initial peak in 1968 was associated with a period of sunny and reasonably warm weather. The subsequent period with low visiting rates was cold and misty and was also initiated by me with mist-netting on the lek.

Most resident males seem to settle on only one lek during a particular season, though a few males, such as male 1 and male 2 in 1968, may go from one lek to another in the course of a season. Male 1 even succeeded in defending residences on three different leks in three different periods of the same season (1968). Many resident males return to the same lek in the following year. Out of 54 resident males, ringed in Roderwolde, 30 (56%) were seen in the following year on the same lek. Two males, Fireman and Bib, spent five seasons in succession on the same lek (lek B). Two males were found to have returned after moving to leks some distance away. I observed one male (male 8) on the lek near Boerakker, two years after ringing on lek B in Roderwolde, 12 km away. Another male, ringed on lek D, was observed in the next year on two leks: near Sebaldeburen and Boerakker, both about 13 km away, and about 3.5 km from each other. To give an example of the faithfulness of resident males over years, Table 3 summarizes all observations in the various seasons and on the various leks, for the 21 resident males from lek B in Roderwolde in 1968.

Table 3 The presence of resident males of lek B, Roderwolde 1968, in the years before and after 1968.

Name of male	1966	1967	1968	1969	1970	1971	1972
Boss	A?	A?	B	B			
Grandpa	B	B	B	B			
Yellow-face	B?	B	B				
Orange-face	B?	B	B	B			
Fireman	B	B	B	B	B		
Bib	B	B	B	B	B		
Fan-male	B	B	B	B			
1	B?	B	A/B/E	A/B	B		
2	A?	A?	A/B				
3	B?	B?	B				
4			B	B?			
5			B				
6	A?	A?	B	B?	B?	A?	A?
7	B?	B	B	D			
8			B	—	Bo	Bo	Bo
9			B				
10	A?	A?	B				
11			B/E				
12			B	D	D		
13			B				
14			B				

Key: A, lek A Roderwolde; B, lek B Roderwolde; D, lek D Roderwolde; E, lek E Roderwolde; Bo, lek Boerakker; ?, probably the same as in 1968; —, not seen; connected by underlining, certainly the same male.

Lek B near Roderwolde, end of May 1968. Resident males in oblique postures. From left to right: Fireman (behind), Yellow-face, male 12, Grandpa, and Boss.

Behaviour among resident males

During their stay on the lek, resident males spend a considerable amount of time on comfort behaviour and at rest. They may pay short visits to the edge of the water to bathe, preen on their residences, sleep with their bills in the feathers, sit, stand, or adopt a quiet display attitude: the normal *oblique posture* (Figure 14). When they are disturbed by humans or predators they may adopt an *upright posture* (Figure 14). In the event of a serious disturbance the males may utter repeated short, soft, groaning alarm calls, shortly before and while abandoning the lek.

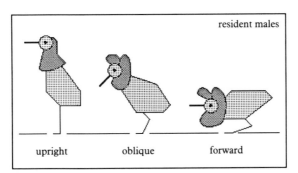

FIGURE 14 *Three postures displayed by resident males when other sorts of males, and females, are absent.*

While only resident males are present on the lek, this relaxed atmosphere between them sometimes disappears, usually for very short periods, although in the early morning such explosions of activity may last somewhat longer. During these periods of mutual encounters, which suddenly start and stop, most or all of the males on the lek participate. The males may threaten one another from their residences with an *ordinary forward* posture (Figure 14) combined with *bill-thrusting*: a conspicuous repeated thrusting with closed bill in the direction of other males or towards the ground, usually performed in synchrony with other males. Occasionally the males may cross territory borders. In that case a male may charge towards another male and return to his residence before reaching the other. He may also attack the other one, and hit his opponent with one or more pecks with his bill, kicks with his feet, or a real smash with his whole body when attacking from the air. More details on these behaviour patterns can be found in Hogan-Warburg's classic work on the Ruff.

Summary

The resident males are the owners of small territories on a lek. These sites, or residences, only 30–60 cm in diameter, are visible as bare patches of earth or as areas of trampled grass with numerous dabs of white faeces. In the Netherlands residences are established around the middle of April and maintained until the middle of June. Some resident males stay throughout this period at one particular residence, but many males move frequently from one site to another and may be absent for several days between periods of residence occupation. Several resident males only stay for a number of days at a particular lek. Site fidelity of resident males is closely related to mating success, but also to external factors, such as the water level at shore leks, and disturbance. The establishment of new resident males mostly occurs by their occupying vacant residences at the border of a lek, followed by their gradual move to the centre if vacancies arise. This is mostly accompanied by fights with prospective neighbours. Less often, new resident males establish themselves by means of a major dispute with the previous possessor of a central residence. The movements of the different resident males from and towards the lek are often synchronized. They stay almost the whole day at the lek. Visiting rates remain high throughout the season. Most resident males settle on only one lek during a season. Some males maintain residences on different leks, but never at the same time. Many resident males remain faithful to the same lek for up to five successive seasons. During their stay on a lek much time is spent on comfort behaviour and rest. During the absence of non-territorial males or females, resident males may adopt a variety of display postures and may occasionally fight.

2.3 SATELLITE MALES

On 7 May 1968 the seven resident males spent a total of 1103 minutes on lek B in Roderwolde during three hours of observation. They were not the only visitors that morning. I saw quite a number of other males on the lek. The sum duration of their visits was 472 minutes, about 30% of the time spent by all males together. Most of these visits (308 minutes altogether) were by males who usually stayed close to the resident males, often for quite long periods (minutes or dozens of minutes) on a residence with its owner, without fighting with that owner. These visitors could also switch from one residence to another without being attacked by the resident males. They were usually tolerated by the residence owners, and often seemed to play the role of companion to the major male on the residence. For that reason they have been called *satellites* by Lidy Hogan-Warburg.

> On the day in question I saw at least five satellite males. Two of them had a large, almost plain white ruff with white head-tufts. They only differed in the colour of their wattles (orange versus yellow) and the colour of their back feathers (light grey versus brown). The third satellite had a small white ruff with orange head-tufts, the fourth had a very small white ruff and tiny head-tufts, and the fifth one was fairly dark.

Almost all the satellites I saw that season, and in others, had similar plumage characteristics: white ruffs and head-tufts, and sometimes white ruffs with orange, reddish or brown head-tufts. Occasionally I saw satellites with different shades of brown or even black in their ruffs as transverse stripes, patches, bibs or fans, but the variability between individual satellites was much smaller than between individual resident males. Hence, individual identification of satellite males was difficult, the more so since I did not succeed in catching many satellites for colour ringing. These males walked rather carefully from one residence to another and my snares, which were excellent for the fast-running resident males during charges or attacks on neighbours, were not the most suitable equipment for catching the prudent satellite males. An extra complicating factor was that most satellites visited the lek when activity was high, when I had to keep my eyes open for things other than individual plumage patterns. Finally, identification was also hindered, since satellites had no strong bonds to particular places, either to residences or to leks. Most of my records only contain information about the number of satellites present on the lek at a particular moment, and about which residences they visited. For only one satellite male can I give a fairly complete picture of his visiting rate to lek B during the 1968 season as well as during the preceding season. He was the one with the little white ruff and orange head-tufts. This male, called *Little-boy*, was the most interesting satellite male I ever saw in the field. The data on all the other satellites I observed could not be fully analysed, because so many records were of anonymous birds.

One early morning on lek B

During the early morning of 7 May 1968 I was reasonably successful in tracking individual satellites.

> One of the males with a large white ruff and white head-tufts, *White-1*, spent almost the

whole morning on the lek. He was already present when I arrived at 4.00, and was still on the lek when I left my observation post at 7.00. He departed only once from the lek at 6.39, in company with a female, another satellite, and two resident males. He remained absent for 11 minutes. The other white male with a large ruff, *White-2*, paid nine different visits to the lek during the observation period of 180 minutes. He spent a total of 62 minutes on lek B. The male with the orange head-tufts, *Little-boy*, spent 61 minutes on the lek spread over five different visits. The male with a small white ruff visited the lek only once for 12 minutes, and the dark male was also seen for only one visit, lasting 10 minutes. The fluctuations in the number of satellites during this observation session were shown in Figure 7.

During the first half hour of my stay it was still too dark to determine the exact location of the satellites. During the remaining 150 minutes White-1 visited a residence 40 times and spent 97% of his time there (Table 4). White-2 paid 22 visits to a residence (during eight visits to the lek), and spent 92% of his time there. Little-boy paid 24 visits to a residence (during five visits to the lek), taking up 90% of his time. The male with a very small ruff did not visit any residence, and the dark satellite spent the whole time he was on the lek on two different residences. White-1 displayed a pronounced preference for the residence of Orange-face. He made 13 visits there (out of 40 visits to residences in total), and 66% of the time he was on the lek was spent there. He also made nine visits (11% of his time) to the residence of Boss and nine visits (13% of his time) to the residence of Fireman. White-2 seemed to have a preference for the residence of Yellow-face. Although he paid only four visits to it, he spent 40% of his time there. He

Table 4 Lek B, Roderwolde, 7 May 1968, 4.30–7.00 a.m. (150 minutes): spatial distribution of three satellite males.

	White-1	White-2	Little-boy
On lek:			
number of times	2	8	5
number of minutes	139	53	61
Number of visits on residence (% of time on lek):			
Boss	9 (11%)	3 (11%)	8 (52%)
Grandpa	2 (2%)	3 (9%)	4 (5%)
Yellow-face	6 (5%)	4 (40%)	1 (0%)
Orange-face	13 (66%)	5 (23%)	5 (18%)
Fireman	9 (13%)	1 (1%)	0 (—)
Bib	1 (0%)	5 (6%)	6 (15%)
Fan-male	0 (—)	1 (2%)	0 (—)
Total	40 (97%)	22 (92%)	24 (90%)
Visits not on residences (% of time on lek):	2 (3%)	5 (8%)	6 (10%)

also made five visits (23% of his time) to the residence of Orange-face. Little-boy displayed a preference for the residence of Boss. He paid eight visits to it and spent 52% of his time there. Little-boy also visited the residences of Orange-face (on five occasions, 18% of his time) and Bib (on six occasions, 15% of his time) relatively often. One can conclude from this that satellite males exhibit a certain degree of site preference, although not nearly so much nor so exclusively as resident males.

Presence on leks

Lidy Hogan-Warburg asserted that satellite males most often visit the small leks, because the resident males on large leks would be less tolerant. She supposed that there were fundamental differences in social organization between small and large leks, but could not give quantitative support for this. Her hypothesis was one of the basic questions in my study on the Ruff. To be able to test the idea I made observations on many leks of various sizes. The data all suggest that the processes on large leks do *not* differ from those on small ones. To get a feeling for the relationship between lek size and visiting rate by satellites, I calculated for each season the average number of resident and satellite males present on a lek. For the seven leks I observed during 1969–1971, I obtained 191 hours of observation data. The results, which are plotted in Figure 15, clearly show that the large leks are visited by many more satellites than the small leks. The figure suggests, however, that the proportion of satellites on a lek is roughly constant, and thus independent of lek size.

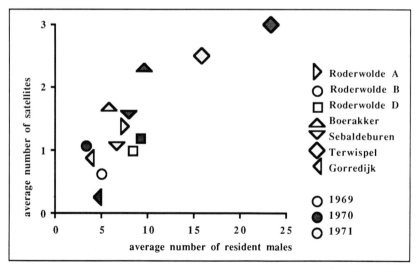

FIGURE 15 *The relationship between the average numbers of satellites and resident males on the various leks in different seasons.*

Visiting rates of satellites to the same lek or to the same residences vary over time, both during single observation sessions and on longer time-scales (see Figures 12 and 13). Early in the season satellites usually start to visit a lek after the establishment of the first resident males, around the middle of April. Then the average number of satellite males present on the lek rises quickly, and may remain high up to the end of May. During the final stage of lekking, in the first half of June, the satellites seldom join leks.

Presence on residences

Roughly 80% of the time that satellite males were on leks was spent on residences. The location of the sites taken up by the satellites on a lek varies during the course of the season. Resident males who are often visited by the satellites during a certain period may get many fewer visits during later periods, whereas other resident males receive more satellite visits.

> For instance, from 15 to 24 April 1968 on lek B satellites spent most of their time with Boss, Orange-face and Yellow-face. During the next 10 days from 25 April to 4 May their preference for Boss further increased. From 5 to 14 May Orange-face became highly preferred. From 15 to 24 May Grandpa became the favoured host of the satellites. From 25 May to 3 June the satellites spent most time with male 12, and during the last period, from 4 to 13 June, with male 13. Also, different satellite males may display different preferences for hosts. For instance, for most of the time Little-boy displayed a very strong preference for Boss, except from 15 to 24 May, when Yellow-face got most of his visits, and from 4 to 13 June, when he displayed a special bond with Fireman.

Resident males may be visited by more than one satellite at the same time. On lek B in 1969 I amassed a total of 10 612 minutes of observation data of resident males on their residences before 7.00. In 88.5% of this sample, the resident male was not accompanied by a satellite. The resident male had one satellite on his residence for 10% of his time, two for 1.4% of his time, three for 0.1% of his time, and as many as four for 0.01% of his time (only one minute of his total time in residence).

Satellite males are not so strongly attached as resident males to a particular lek. In Roderwolde I often saw them changing between lek A and B, and in the season with a tower close to lek D (1971) I was also able to see them flying from lek A to D or vice versa. The attachment to a lek seems to be promoted by positive experiences, such as copulations, and to be weakened by negative experiences, such as trapping. During the years of my study I ringed eight satellites. Following capture, only three of these continued to visit the same lek at the same rate. All three had copulated on the lek before being caught. One of the satellites continued to visit another lek in the same area, but disappeared from the lek where he was ringed. One satellite was only occasionally seen after capture and the other three were not re-sighted after being ringed.

Most satellites seem to visit a particular lek for one season only. None of the ringed satellites were seen in the seasons after ringing. Nevertheless, on the basis of precise plumage descriptions, I believe that certain satellite males do visit the same lek for several seasons in succession.

For instance, in 1966 and 1967 leks A and B were visited by an unmarked male whose plumage was identical to that of Little-boy (ringed in 1968), and who, especially in 1967, also behaved like Little-boy. Also in 1966 and 1967 this bird succeeded in securing a major share of the satellite copulations. Thus, it is very likely that the bird observed in 1966 and 1967 was in fact Little-boy, and that he visited lek B for three successive seasons.

Interactions between satellites and resident males

Satellite males usually fly into the lek. They may land directly on a residence, but may also land between residences or at the edge of the lek. When staying, or moving on or around particular residences, satellite males may be attacked by the owners, but when there are only resident males and satellites present such attacks are not very serious. Certain satellites are able to endure these attacks, but most individuals avoid them by visiting tolerant resident males. Little-boy endured many attacks, and was therefore able to spend much time with Boss, who was not very tolerant towards satellites. Most other satellites did not visit Boss for this very reason, and spent most time with more tolerant resident males, such as Grandpa and Orange-face.

On joining the residence of a tolerant resident male, a satellite, while facing the resident male, usually adopts the normal oblique posture (Figure 16), which differs slightly from the oblique posture of resident males. The resident male holds his bill in a conspicuous way in front of his body, while the satellite holds his bill partially concealed in his ruff. Tolerant resident males usually react to an arriving satellite by adopting the *squat posture* (Figure 16), in which the body is held horizontally, pressed against the ground, the head is turned away from the satellite, and the bill is held vertically against the ground. The resident male may freeze in this posture for several seconds or even minutes. Then, he may gradually rise from the ground, adopt the *half-squat posture* (Figure 16), in which the position of the body axis is not altered, and further rise to the *oblique posture* (Figure 16). Both males may stay together for long periods, several minutes up to an hour. When satellite and resident face each other in the oblique posture, the resident male may occasionally perform bill-thrusting towards the satellite, who may then react by adopting the *tiptoe posture* (Figure 16), in which the body axis is held vertically, and the shape of the ruff is changed such that the bill is almost completely concealed. This posture may also be adopted by the satellite before leaving the residence, during a move from one residence to another, or during a stay on the lek outside the residences. Certain satellite males, especially those suffering many attacks from resident males, may stay at the border of the lek, and assume the tiptoe or the upright posture (Figure 14).

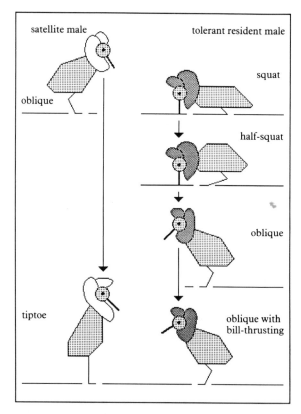

FIGURE 16 *The postures of satellites and resident males during visits by satellites to tolerant resident males.*

When joining the residence of an intolerant resident male, the satellite male immediately adopts the squat posture (Figure 17). The resident male positions himself opposite the satellite and also adopts the squat posture (Figure 17), usually with his bill on the head of the satellite. The squat posture of the resident male may be maintained for several seconds or even minutes. The posture may be interrupted by the *spread-tail forward posture* (Figure 17), which strongly resembles the forward posture used by resident males, but differs in that the wings are held somewhat away from the body, thereby conspicuously exposing the spread white tail feathers. While adopting this forward posture, the resident male turns in front of his visitor, continuously facing him. The resident male thus moves opposite to the squatting satellite male, to and fro over a semi-circle around the satellite's head. This forward posture is always combined with bill-thrusting, sometimes with pecking towards the head of the satellite, aimed primarily at the wattles around the bill, and occasionally escalates to an outright

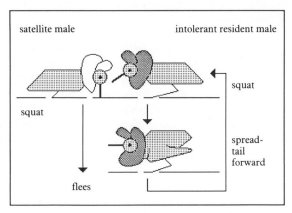

FIGURE 17 *The postures of satellites and resident males during visits by satellites to intolerant resident males.*

attack on the satellite. Certain satellites endure this treatment for fairly long periods, but many others leave after a short stay. A visit to the residence of an intolerant male is only possible when the satellite male persists in adopting the squat posture, and submits to the intimidation by the resident male.

Lek B near Roderwolde, 1967. Fan-male in front, Orange-face just behind him, white satellite in the tiptoe posture on the left, and in the middle background Grandpa while bill-thrusting.

The benefits of submission

One might question whether satellite males are masochistic – whether they enjoy being the subject of many attacks – or, alternatively, whether the cost of being pecked and attacked by resident males is compensated for by some kind of benefit. This latter possibility seems to be real. Satellite males may obtain copulations on leks, but mainly on the residences of successful resident males. Usually these males are very intolerant towards satellites, especially when they are visited by females. A resident male is generally unable to copulate when there is a satellite on his residence, because almost all copulation attempts fail due to interference by the satellite male. The satellite on such residences, however, may exploit a very brief absence of the resident male, for instance during an attack on a neighbour, to perform a copulation.

In 1968 I saw 16 copulations by satellites on lek B in Roderwolde. Twelve of these copulations were performed by Little-boy. Boss was the most successful resident male that season. He secured 45 out of the 85 copulations performed by resident males, but he was also the most aggressive towards satellites. Little-boy was the only satellite able to endure Boss's attacks and thus succeeded in obtaining 10 copulations on that residence. One other satellite achieved a copulation there. The remaining copulations by satellites were performed on the residences of Fireman (2), Yellow-face (2), and Grandpa (1), the three most successful resident males after Boss. These resident males were seen to copulate 14, nine, and five times respectively.

Constancy of status

It may be dangerous to conclude on the basis of field data alone that the status of an individual (resident male or satellite) is constant over the years. In the large sample of resident males that I was able to trace over a number of successive seasons, I did not observe any change of status. Nor were status changes seen in the small sample of satellite males visiting my leks in successive years. Nevertheless, the resulting conclusion, that status changes do not occur, may be wrong because the sample of satellites is too small, or because a change of status might be associated with a change of domicile. There are three lines of evidence, however, which, taken together, support the view that status *is* constant over several years. First, none of the male Ruffs in an experimental, aviary population consistently changed its status during a stay of several years. Temporary changes of status, however, seem to be possible. These, and more details concerning the experimental population, will be discussed later in this section. Second, all males in the experimental population kept the same plumage characteristics over the years. The same holds for all ringed males in the field seen during successive seasons. Finally, all field data show that the plumage types of satellites can be distinguished almost completely from those of the resident males.

Role-switching

One might question whether satellites adopt their 'submissive' role because they are unable to fight or are less able to defend a residence than are resident males. It is not easy to confirm this possibility, or to reject the alternative that satellites are equally as strong as resident males. On a lek I sometimes saw satellites chase and attack other satellite males and other non-territorial males. However, attacks on resident males by satellites are extremely rare, though not completely absent.

Observations of males who have not yet developed their nuptial plumage, called *naked-nape males* by Lidy Hogan-Warburg, suggest that these individuals are able to switch roles. Naked-nape males are usually only one year old. They rarely visit a lek for more than a few days, and thus may be free-ranging or on migration. They often possess the dark plumage characteristics of resident males. During a visit to the lek they may stay at the border and interact aggressively with each other, but they may also approach resident males in the half-squat posture, often without being attacked. When arriving on a residence, they immediately adopt the squat posture, and thus behave like a satellite on the residence of an intolerant resident male. Usually the resident male then also squats. While the naked-nape male squats, the resident male may interrupt his squat posture with the spread-tail forward posture, combined with turning, bill-thrusting, and pecking. Occasionally the resident male treats the naked-nape male as a female and even tries to copulate with his visitor. Conversely, during the squat posture of the resident male, the naked-nape male may adopt the half-squat posture, turn, and try to copulate with the resident male or another naked-nape male on the same residence.

A remarkable case history

Switching of roles has also been observed in adult satellite males. The most remarkable example concerns Little-boy, who defended a residence for a few days during the absence of its owner. This happened in 1968 on lek B in the second half of May. Around the middle of May Little-boy was frequently present on the lek and spent much time together with Boss, Yellow-face, or Bib, or stayed alone. He was seen to copulate on the residences of Boss and Yellow-face. Little-boy was fairly aggressive during this period. He often charged and attacked non-territorial males, but he was also subject to aggression by resident males, especially Bib and Fireman. At the same time Bib was not so often present as the other resident males. At certain times he left his residence for considerable periods.

On 18 May Bib did not return to his residence (see also Figure 10). Instead, Little-boy spent almost all the time he was on the lek on Bib's residence. Quite often he was visited by his neighbour, Orange-face, and then behaved as a normal satellite. Occasionally he was visited by other satellite males. Then he behaved as a residence owner towards a visiting satellite. The next day, 19 May, Little-boy spent as much time as the resident males on the lek. He was no longer visited by his neighbours, but frequently by other satellites, who were treated as if by any other residence owner. In addition, Little-boy was very aggressive towards non-territorial males at the border of the lek.

In the late afternoon of that day I received two guests who wanted to see the display of the ruffs: Gavin (a Scot) and Helga (an Austrian), both acquainted with the lek behaviour of Black Grouse. We all slept in the large sleeping tent that night. It was freezing and Helga suffered badly from the cold. The next morning we decided that Helga would go with me to the observation tent close to lek B, and Gavin, who had visited me before, would stay on the other side of the canal in a tent on a platform. There was no wind when we entered our hides at 4.00, and it was rather misty, especially above the canal.

Initially the situation on the lek was the same as on the previous day. Little-boy stayed on Bib's residence and all resident males from the previous day were also present. Little-boy admitted satellites and behaved like a residence owner to his guests. He further attacked non-territorial males who came too close to his quarters. However, at 5.30 Bib returned to the lek after an absence of two to three days. Bib tried to occupy his residence, but was attacked by Little-boy. Both males became engaged in a long fight, occasionally interrupted by short pauses, altogether lasting about 10 minutes. This fight was as intense as those in which a resident male was displaced from his residence by a newcomer. In the end Little-boy lost the encounter and left the residence, but did not depart from the lek. Instead, to my great surprise, he started to visit the residences of Boss, Fireman, and Yellow-face, and resumed the behaviour of a satellite. At 6.00 Little-boy returned to Bib's residence, where he also continued to play the role of a normal satellite.

I believe that this was the most impressive sequence of Ruff behaviour I ever saw, although I was not fully aware of it at the time. Anyway, Helga had a very exciting morning in Roderwolde. She forgot the low temperatures, which, thankfully, rapidly rose to a very pleasant level around 8.00. Gavin, however, had very bad luck. He could not see anything until 6.30 because of the mist over the canal and could only establish that Bib returned and that Little-boy had given up his residence. Helga and I had to give him a lengthy explanation of the events during our second breakfast in a warm and sunny meadow.

After this take-over by the original residence owner, Little-boy continued to visit lek B frequently, though I never again saw any tendency for him to establish a territory. However, he still occasionally performed charges and attacks on non-territorial males, other satellites included. He was subsequently seen obtaining two copulations on Boss's residence during the final part of the season.

Role-switching in an aviary

A change in behaviour, reminiscent of role-switching, was also observed in a satellite male held in an aviary with a number of females. From 1964 to 1979 a small population of Ruffs was maintained at the Zoology Department of the University of Groningen. This population was set up by Lidy Hogan-Warburg, and, after her departure to Canada, continued by Jaap Kruijt. The birds were kept for the study of the inheritance of status in males. At that time techniques for analysing the descent of an individual, such as the electrophoresis of proteins and DNA fingerprinting, were not yet very advanced. To answer the question whether differences in status are the result of genetic differences, one had to study the offspring of specified parents. However, male Ruffs do not care for their offspring, which makes it difficult to recognize the father–offspring relationship. Furthermore, female Ruffs may copulate with more than one male. This limits the value of, for instance, a study of similarities between the phenotypes of siblings collected in the field. In the experimental population, single males were placed together with small groups of females over several seasons. A satellite was treated likewise. In the previous season, when all the males were held together, this male clearly behaved like a satellite. He did not display any site attachment, and visited resident males who formed a lek-like community at a fixed location in the large aviary. In the seasons when the satellite was the only male in a group, however, he developed a kind of site attachment, which strongly resembled the behaviour of resident males on single-male leks.

Although the experimental population did not yield many data on the inheritance of status, it did produce some other interesting results. It revealed, for instance, that satellite males are able to fight, that they do really fight during particular stages of their yearly cycle, and that they are able to obtain a high rank in the dominance hierarchy of males. In the years when all experimental males were held in the same group, there was much competition amongst them around the food containers during autumn and winter. In most cases satellite males occupied the space around these containers and also displayed much aggressive behaviour. All the other males were vigorously attacked when they approached these areas. Foraging by the sub-dominant resident males was only possible when many birds assembled in the area around the container. In the beginning of April the behaviour of satellites changed. They gradually dropped their claim to the area around the food containers, became less aggressive, and wandered more throughout the whole cage. Meanwhile, the resident males became more aggressive, but the site preference developed by them was not clearly associated with the distribution of food.

Fighting ability

In many species, for instance the Common Toad (*Bufo bufo*) and Red Deer (*Cervus elaphus*), the ability of an individual to win a fight is related to body size. It is reasonable to believe that the same relationship holds for the Ruff. Thus, a comparison of body size between resident males and satellites may offer clear indications about the relative fighting ability of satellite males. Such data have been collected by L.N. Dobrinskij in northern Siberia, by Robert Gibson in the collection of Ruffs in the British Museum, and by myself in the field. The data from Siberia and the British Museum do not include details about the behavioural status of males on a lek. The status of the males concerned was deduced from their plumage characteristics, and in Section 2.5 I shall go into the objections to this derivation. My own data do include the details of behavioural status on the lek. Dobrinskij found in a sample of 720 males that the dark ones (365 altogether, probably all resident males) were approximately 4.5% heavier (average weight 197.7 g) than the non-dark males (average weight 188.6 g; 355 individuals, which included the satellites). Further, the heart and kidneys of the dark males were larger than those of the non-dark ones. Gibson measured the wing length of 45 museum specimens, probably 37 resident males and eight satellites. He found that satellite wing length was about 2.5% less (average length 178 mm) than the resident male's wing length (average length 182 mm), a statistically significant difference. My own data on the wing lengths of birds caught for ringing also revealed a difference of 2.5% between resident males and satellites. The average length in the sample of 63 resident males was 194 mm, and in nine satellite males 189 mm. These findings all suggest that satellite males are less able than resident males to win a fight, but they do not alter the fact that satellite males may be experienced fighters.

Summary

Satellite males, which distinguish themselves from resident males by their light plumage, are not bound to specific territories. They rarely display aggressive behaviour, but approach the residences owned by resident males, behave submissively and may be tolerated by the owners. If the resident male is tolerant towards the satellite, the latter may adopt the oblique and upright postures. If the resident male is not tolerant, the satellite must freeze in a squatting posture and endure pecks by the owner to acquire a position on the residence. The resident males which get most matings are least tolerant towards satellites. Only some satellites are able to endure this intolerance, yet most satellite matings occur on these residences. A satellite male does not spend so much time on a lek as a resident male. Most satellite visits occur during the early morning and afternoon. Fluctuations through the season in the visiting rate of satellites to a particular lek are closely related to fluctuations in visiting rates of resident males, marginal males and females. Satellite visiting rate is positively related to lek size. The location of the sites taken by the satellites on a lek changes through a season. Also, different satellites may display different preferences for sites on the lek. Yet different satellites may select the same residence at the same time, and up to four different satellites may be present on a single residence. Satellite males usually visit several leks during the same season, but they rarely seem to visit the same lek in successive seasons. The status of satellites and independent males is not interchangeable, as is shown by the constancy of status of experimental males held in an aviary, from the constancy of the plumage of these males and of ringed males in the field, and from consistent differences between the plumage characteristics of satellites and those of independent males observed in the field. Temporary changes of status only occur in under-developed naked-nape males, and, under exceptional circumstances, also in adult males, for instance during an absence of several days of a usual host, and in a situation without any resident males. Satellite males are able to fight, especially during the winter period, but their ability to win a fight is probably lower than in resident males because of their smaller body size.

2.4 MARGINAL MALES

The males visiting lek B in Roderwolde on 7 May 1968 were not only resident males and satellites. Individuals of a third (and final) category spent altogether 164 minutes (10.4% of the total time spent by males) at the border of the lek. Males belonging to this category, the *marginal males*, did not defend a particular site on the lek and did not remain close to the territories of resident males. When approaching these territories, they were immediately attacked by the owners. Marginal males seemed to stand in awe of the resident males and rarely displayed any resistance when attacked by a territory owner. They mostly escaped when chased and avoided physical confrontation. Most marginal males had only partially developed plumage, though some had full nuptial plumage. The colours and patterns of the marginal males' plumage did not differ from those of the resident males.

Presence on leks

The average number of marginal males present on a lek during a whole season is not clearly related to the average number of resident males, nor to the average number of satellites present on that lek. Thus, in the process of lek selection, marginal males seem to show similar preferences for small and large leks and do not appear to be influenced by the number of males present on the leks. In the timing of visits to a particular lek, however, they do show patterns similar to those of satellites (see Figures 12 and 13). This holds both for changes in visiting rate during the course of a day and for changes in the course of the season.

> The data collected on 7 May 1968 give an example of the changes in visiting rates on a shorter time-scale (see Figure 7). During three hours of observation I counted 35 visits by a marginal male to lek B, involving at least 10 individuals. One of them, with black ruff and head-tufts, paid at least six visits to the lek during which he stayed for 42 minutes. Another bird, with a white ruff and black head-tufts, made three visits lasting 16 minutes on the lek. All other individuals probably made fewer visits and spent less time on the lek. They stayed too short a time to be described properly and thus joined the ranks of the anonymous mass.

Behaviour

I never observed a copulation by a marginal male. In view of the large number of copulations that I saw other males perform, it seems that the probability of their copulating on a lek is very low. This might be one reason for marginal males not to develop strong ties with a particular lek. In Roderwolde I frequently saw them flying from one lek to another, regardless of the distance between leks. In the great majority of cases, the presence of a marginal male on a particular lek seems to be confined to one or a few brief visits, especially for marginal males with poorly developed nuptial plumage. Marginal males with fully developed plumage, however, may visit the lek more often, and may gradually change their behaviour from extremely fearful to rather aggressive. Occasionally such a change takes place in the course of only one or a few visits to the lek. In these cases a marginal male may settle on a new residence on the lek, or usurp the residence of an established male, switching its status to that of a resident male. Thus, the status of resident and marginal male may be interchanged.

On arriving at the edge of the lek, a marginal male usually adopts an upright posture (see Figure 14). A resident male often reacts to the arrival of such a marginal male with bill-thrusting from his residence, but also with a more serious charge in the direction of the marginal male, a real attack, or with chasing after the marginal male. Marginal males, standing in an upright posture at the side of the lek, always avoid bodily contact with resident males. They flee when attacked or chased, and may even fly off in response to the bill-thrusting of the resident, who stays on his residence.

A marginal male who regularly visits the lek and seems to be in the process of establishing his own territory may land closer to the existing residences or even occupy an empty residence, and adopt the normal oblique posture (see Figure 14). Such marginal males may elicit bill-thrusting from neighbouring residents, but they do not suffer such a high rate of attacks as the marginal males in the upright posture. When attacked, however, these marginal males likewise tend to avoid bodily contact with resident males. Even though these marginal males rarely counterattack, they may take evasive action by moving towards another site on the lek, and do not leave the lek as quickly as the marginal males from the periphery.

When a lek is visited by more than one marginal male at the same time, these different individuals are usually widely separated. Occasionally, however, marginal males may interact with one another. In these cases they may show all the behaviour patterns which occur in encounters between resident males, even to the extent of attacking each other.

Changes of status

In contrast to the numerous transitions I saw between marginal and resident males, I never observed a permanent change from marginal status to satellite or vice versa. Temporary changes in marginal males, which were characterized by the appearance of certain aspects of the behaviour of satellites, have only been observed in the so-called naked-nape males with very poorly developed nuptial plumage (see Section 2.3). These males, however, have not reached the same maturity as most other males on a lek. It is possible that the behaviour of an individual is more flexible at particular stages during its life, for instance when young and during migratory activity, than at other stages, such as in full adulthood and when reproductively mature. Thus, there is justification for distinguishing between two main categories of males: resident and marginal males on the one hand, and satellites on the other. Males of both resident and marginal status are called *independent males*. Permanent (or semi-permanent) transitions within the class of independent males occur very regularly. Permanent transitions between independent males and satellites, however, seem to be impossible.

Summary

Marginal males stay at the border of the lek. Variation in their plumage colour is similar to that in resident males, but their plumage may be less well developed. They visit the lek occasionally, especially when many other individuals (satellites and females) are present, but they do not seem to prefer leks with many resident males to small leks. Marginal males have never been seen to copulate on leks. They are frequently attacked by resident males, and usually respond by escaping or adopting the upright posture. They may attack other marginal males. Transitions between marginal and resident males are frequently observed, but permanent transitions between marginal and satellite status do not seem to be possible. Temporary transitions between these latter classes have only been observed in naked-nape males.

2.5 PLUMAGE DIVERSITY

When watching ruffs, one does not get the impression of a group of anonymous birds, but rather of witnessing complex interactions between individuals, each recognizable by its own particular nuptial plumage. During the late summer, autumn, and winter, male Ruffs can only be distinguished from females by their larger size. In spring, however, the males develop their characteristic nuptial plumage, and in the Dutch population this occurs between the middle of March and the end of April. The most remarkable feature of this plumage is the large collar of feathers behind the face which covers the breast and neck of the bird (see Figure 8). The feathers of a ruff emerge from a continuous area including chin, throat, and cheeks, bordered by feather-tracts running the length of both sides of the neck. These collars of feathers, which greatly contribute to individual diversity, may have various brilliant colours and several alternative

Lek B near Roderwolde, 1967. From left to right: Fireman, Grandpa (low), Yellow-face, Bib with Fan-male in front of him, and male 1.

patterns. A second characteristic of this nuptial plumage is the presence of two tufts of feathers behind the eyes, emerging from the rear of the crown. The colours and patterns of these tufts vary almost to the same extent as those of the collar. A third variable is the absence of feathers at the base of the bill and on the area around the eyes, which is covered with wattle-like structures of the skin instead of feathers. These wattles may also vary in colour between individuals. Moreover, the colours of the legs and bill are variable, and finally the darkness and shade of the feathers on the back and the upper side of the tail and wings may also differ between individuals.

Interrelations of plumage characteristics

The variety of colours and patterns of male Ruffs has drawn the attention of numerous investigators. Andersen noticed as early as 1948 that the colours of ruff and head-tufts in 39 males he caught on Tipperne in Denmark were not independent of each other. Males with white ruffs usually had white head-tufts and males with non-white ruffs mostly possessed non-white head-tufts. He confirmed this trend by analysing the males in the collection at the Zoological Museum of Copenhagen (64 specimens).

An analysis by Goethe, of a sample of 80 males shot in the 1930s in southern Belorussia (Pripet Marshes), did not show a similar relationship between the

Table 5 The analysis by Goethe of the plumage colours of males shot in southern Belorussia around 1935.

	Head-tufts			
	Black + Grey	Coloured	White	Totals
Ruff				
Black + Grey	19 (16.2)	15 (17.5)	1 (1.3)	35
Coloured	11 (13.4)	18 (14.5)	0 (1.1)	29
White	7 (7.4)	7 (8.0)	2 (0.6)	16
Totals	37	40	3	80

Note: numbers in brackets are expected values given a random combination.

colours of the ruff and head-tufts (Table 5). The observed numbers of birds in nine categories of plumage were almost identical to the numbers expected if colours of ruff and head-tufts were independent of each other. However, the lack of correlation could be due to the small number of males with white ruffs in Goethe's material. However, there are other striking correlations between ruff and head-tufts in his data. For instance, all 20 males with transverse striping on the ruff possessed head-tufts of precisely the same basic colour as the ruff (11 black and nine coloured). In contrast, all 10 males with plain black ruffs possessed coloured head-tufts, and 12 out of 18 males with coloured ruffs that

Table 6 The analysis by Shepard of the plumage colours of males observed in northern Sweden in 1970.

	Head-tufts			
	Black + Grey	Coloured	White	Totals
Ruff				
Black + Grey	22 (21.1)	16 (18.0)	6 (4.8)	44
Coloured	18 (15.4)	14 (13.1)	0 (3.5)	32
White	8 (11.5)	11 (9.8)	5 (2.6)	24
Totals	48	41	11	100

Note: numbers in brackets are expected values given a random combination.

were plain or had small or large irregular patches or dashes possessed black head-tufts.

The lack of a relationship between the colour of the ruff and the colour of the head-tufts is not restricted to Goethe's material. In a sample of 100 males observed on leks in northern Sweden and described by Shepard, both features also seem to combine at random (Table 6). In most other data sets, however, there seem to be strong correlations. For instance, in a sample of 110 males shot in northern Germany and described by Drenckhahn, the colours of the ruff and head-tufts tend to be the same (Table 7).

The same phenomenon can be found in the plumage types described by Hogan-Warburg (Table 8) for a sample of 214 males observed on leks in the Netherlands. In the categories with similar colours on both parts of the nuptial plumage, the observed numbers of birds are all higher than the numbers expected if both colours were independent of each other. The numbers of birds in the categories with dissimilar plumage are all lower than the expected

Table 7 The analysis by Drenckhahn of the plumage colours of males shot in northern West Germany before 1975.

	Head-tufts			
	Black + Grey	Coloured	White	Totals
Ruff				
Black + Grey	18 (14.2)	8 (13.2)	8 (6.5)	34
Coloured	12 (15.4)	23 (14.4)	2 (7.1)	37
White	16 (16.3)	12 (15.2)	11 (7.4)	39
Totals	46	43	21	110

Note: numbers in brackets are expected values given a random combination.

Table 8 The analysis by Hogan-Warburg of the plumage colours of males observed in the northern part of the Netherlands from 1960 to 1963.

	Head-tufts			
	Black	Coloured	White	Totals
Ruff				
Black	41 (21.3)	14 (21.3)	5 (17.4)	60
Coloured	14 (16.3)	31 (16.3)	1 (13.3)	46
White	21 (38.4)	31 (38.4)	56 (31.2)	108
Totals	76	76	62	214

Note: numbers in brackets are expected values given a random combination.

numbers, although the difference between observed and expected is small in the group with coloured ruffs and black head-tufts and in the group with white ruffs and coloured head-tufts. Thus certain combinations are very likely (the same colour in both parts), certain combinations are unlikely (a black or a coloured ruff with white head-tufts, and to a lesser extent a white ruff with black head-tufts and a black ruff with coloured head-tufts), and certain combinations seem to occur according to chance. The resemblance between ruff and head-tufts is much better than can be deduced from Table 8. Dark-coloured ruffs are mostly combined with dark-coloured head-tufts, usually of precisely the same colour. Light-coloured ruffs are mostly combined with light-coloured head-tufts. White ruffs with a pattern are most often combined with white head-tufts with a similar pattern. Plain white ruffs are most often combined with plain white head-tufts.

Lindemann described the colouration and the pattern of ruffs only, in a sample of 508 males collected in the late 1930s in four geographical areas: southern Belorussia (Pripet Marshes), northeastern Poland, the Pommerellen

Table 9 The analysis by Lindemann of the ruffs of males observed in eastern Europe around 1935.

	Pattern				
	Plain	Irregular	Coarse regular	Fine regular	Totals
Colour					
Black	42 (41.3)	47 (50.3)	50 (48.2)	36 (35.1)	175
Coloured	48 (43.5)	53 (52.9)	49 (50.7)	34 (36.9)	184
White	30 (35.2)	46 (42.8)	41 (41.1)	32 (29.9)	149
Totals	120	146	140	102	508

Note: numbers in brackets are expected values given a random combination.

Table 10 The analysis by Van Rhijn of the plumage characteristics of males caught in snares on leks in the northern part of the Netherlands from 1968 to 1971.

A. Colour of ruff and head-tufts

| | Head-tufts | | | |
	Black	Coloured	White	Totals
Ruff				
Black	30 (23.0)	20 (25.3)	5 (6.7)	55
Coloured	9 (12.1)	20 (13.3)	0 (3.6)	29
White	2 (5.9)	5 (6.4)	7 (1.7)	14
Totals	41	45	12	98

B. Colour and pattern of ruff

| | Pattern | | | |
	Plain	Irregular	Regular	Totals
Colour				
Black	13 (14.0)	15 (12.9)	27 (28.1)	55
Coloured	5 (7.4)	4 (6.8)	20 (14.8)	29
White	7 (3.6)	4 (3.3)	3 (7.1)	14
Totals	25	23	50	98

C. Pattern of ruff and colour of head-tufts

| | Pattern in ruff | | | |
	Plain	Irregular	Regular	Totals
Head-tufts				
Black	5 (10.5)	4 (9.6)	32 (20.9)	41
Coloured	13 (11.5)	17 (10.5)	15 (23.0)	45
White	7 (3.1)	2 (2.8)	3 (6.1)	12
Totals	25	23	50	98

(near Gdansk, Poland) and Estonia. He distinguished 12 different basic colours and four types of pattern, giving 48 possible combinations, all of which he encountered in the wild. His data strongly suggest that colours and patterns combine at random (Table 9).

My own descriptions of 98 males, caught for ringing, also show obvious relationships between different aspects of the nuptial plumage (Table 10). All

Table 10 Continued.

D. Colour of ruff and wattles

| | Wattles | | | |
	Yellow	Orange	Red	Totals
Ruff				
Black	24 (22.4)	25 (25.3)	6 (7.3)	55
Coloured	11 (11.8)	12 (13.3)	6 (3.8)	29
White	5 (5.7)	8 (6.4)	1 (1.9)	14
Totals	40	45	13	98

E. Pattern of ruff and colour of wattles

| | Colour of wattles | | | |
	Yellow	Orange	Red	Totals
Pattern of ruff				
Plain	9 (10.2)	15 (11.5)	1 (3.3)	25
Irregular	10 (9.4)	9 (10.6)	4 (3.1)	23
Regular	21 (20.4)	21 (23.0)	8 (6.6)	50
Totals	40	45	13	98

F. Colour of head-tufts and wattles

| | Wattles | | | |
	Yellow	Orange	Red	Totals
Head-tufts				
Black	20 (16.7)	17 (18.8)	4 (5.4)	41
Coloured	15 (18.4)	22 (20.7)	8 (6.0)	45
White	5 (4.9)	6 (5.5)	1 (1.6)	12
Totals	40	45	13	98

Note: numbers in brackets are expected values given a random combination.

combinations of similar colours in ruffs and head-tufts occur more often than expected by chance and all combinations of dissimilar colours occur less often (Table 10A). Like the data collected by Lindemann, my study does not imply that the colour and pattern of the ruff are interrelated (Table 10B). By contrast, the pattern of the ruff seems to be related to the colour of the head-tufts (Table 10C). Black head-tufts are combined with regular patterns of transverse striping on the ruff more often than would be expected if both features were independent of each other. Coloured head-tufts are more often combined with irregular patterns on the ruff, and white head-tufts more often with plain ruffs. As with Goethe's data, I found that almost all males with transverse striping on the ruff had ruffs and head-tufts of precisely the same basic colour (43 out of 50). My data further showed, also following Goethe, that most males with black ruffs, plain or with an irregular pattern, possessed coloured head-tufts (19 out of 28). In contrast to Goethe I did not find coloured ruffs that were plain or had an irregular pattern to be more often combined with black head-tufts. Finally, my data offered the possibility of investigating whether the colour of the wattles was related to certain other aspects of the nuptial plumage. My calculations did not, however, show any such relationship. The observed numbers of birds with different combinations of wattle colour on the one hand and ruff colour, ruff pattern, or colour of head-tufts on the other, were almost identical to the numbers expected if wattle colour was independent of the other variables (Tables 10D, 10E and 10F).

When reviewing the various tables in this section, it is plain that the frequencies of the different colours are not identical for ruffs and head-tufts (Tables 5, 6, 7, 8 and 10A). A white basic colour seems to occur more often in ruffs than in head-tufts, whereas a black or a coloured basic colour is usually less common in ruffs than in head-tufts. Hogan-Warburg's data further suggest that the light colours particularly occur much more often in head-tufts than in ruffs.

Analysis of the relationships between the various aspects of the nuptial plumage may offer some clues about the genetic mechanism behind it. For instance, the existence of three different colours (yellow, orange, and red) of the wattles occurring independently of the other plumage characteristics suggests that genes for wattle colour, if they exist, do not influence the other plumage characteristics. Nor do they seem to be linked with the genes influencing them. The distribution of these colours in my sample (Tables 10D, 10E and 10F) further suggest that wattle colour is determined by only one gene. Two alleles, Y (yellow) and R (red) on one locus and in Hardy–Weinberg equilibrium with allele frequencies of 0.64 and 0.36 respectively, would be sufficient to explain the observed frequencies of 40 yellow homozygotes (YY), 45 orange hetero-zygotes (YR), and 13 red homozygotes (RR). If this hypothesis is correct, the expected frequencies deviate by only a few tenths from the observed ones. Reasoning along these lines, the Russian geneticist L.V. Ferri calculated that the variability of plumage characteristics seems to be determined by about seven different genes. However, final proof of these hypotheses requires breeding experiments, and sufficient of these have not been done to date.

Differences between the male categories

The distribution of the plumage characteristics of satellite males is quite distinct from that of independent males, with only a slight overlap occurring between

Lek B near Roderwolde, end of May 1968. From left to right: Yellow-face, male 12, two white satellites on tiptoe, Grandpa, and Boss.

them. Independent males normally possess black or dark-coloured nuptial plumage, satellites mainly the light or white plumage. Hogan-Warburg described 132 independent males and 82 satellites. Her data on the colour of ruff and head-tufts in both groups are summarized in Table 11. Each figure in this table represents the percentage of individuals with a specific combination of colours. The table shows that independent males may possess almost all combinations of colours, and the combination of a black ruff with black head-tufts occurs most often in this group. Combinations such as a coloured ruff with

Table 11 The analysis by Hogan-Warburg of the plumage colours of independent and satellite males observed in the northern part of the Netherlands from 1960 to 1963.

	Head-tufts					
	Independent males			Satellites		
	Black	Coloured	White	Black	Coloured	White
Ruff						
Black	31%	8%	4%	0%	4%	0%
Coloured	11%	19%	0%	0%	7%	1%
White	16%	3%	8%	0%	33%	55%

coloured head-tufts, and a white ruff with black head-tufts, are also common, followed to a lesser extent by a coloured ruff with black head-tufts, a black ruff with coloured head-tufts, and even, very rarely, a white ruff with white head-tufts. Most satellite males possess a white ruff with white head-tufts. A white ruff with coloured head-tufts is the only other combination which is common among satellites. Thus, the variability among satellites is much smaller than that among independent males.

A more detailed analysis of these differences reveals that all independent males with a white ruff and white head-tufts have a pattern on both parts of the plumage, whereas most satellites with a white ruff and white head-tufts are plain white. Birds with a plain white ruff and plain or patterned head-tufts or with plain white head-tufts and a plain or patterned ruff are always satellites. For that reason, this type of plumage has been called *satellite plumage*. The analysis further reveals that black head-tufts are invariably associated with independent status. Combinations of any ruff with black head-tufts have therefore been called *independent plumage*. The remaining combinations do not give a 100% prediction of status, so have been called *atypical plumage*. This does not mean that status is completely unpredictable. For instance, almost all males with a black ruff and non-black head-tufts are independent males, whereas almost all males with a white ruff and coloured head-tufts are satellites. Thus, while plumage can be a good guide to a male's status, it is not an infallible predictor.

Differences between samples

One might wonder why the data collected by certain investigators (Andersen, Drenckhahn, Hogan-Warburg, and myself) lead to the conclusion that the colours of the ruff and head-tufts are interrelated, while the data of others (Goethe and Shepard) do not. Obviously the descriptions of the various investigators of their samples vary and these differences are illustrated in Table 12. It summarizes for 10 samples, described by six different investigators, the percentages of three groups of basic colours of the ruff: black or grey, colour, and white. Although all the samples include a reasonable number of individuals (48–344), the differences between samples are great. The percentage of black or grey varies from 19 to 65, the percentage of colour from 22 to 65, and the percentage of white from 8 to 52.

These contrasts may partly be due to the use of *different criteria* by the investigators. This possibility seems likely, because the different samples from the same investigator do not show such big discrepancies. For example the percentage of black or grey varies only from 19 to 40 in Lindemann's data, the percentage of colour from 42 to 65, and the percentage of white from 8 to 16. The data sets described by Drenckhahn are even more similar to one other.

A second possibility is that the composition of populations may *differ in different places*. This seems likely because the composition of samples collected in different geographical areas by the same investigator may still differ consider-

Table 12 The percentages of ruff colours in 10 samples of males described by six investigators.

Data from	G	L	L	L	L	S	D	D	H	R
Years	±1935	±1935	±1935	±1935	±1935	1970	<1975	1969–1971	1960–1963	1968–1971
Area	sb	sb	nop	pom	est	ns	nwg	nwg	nnl	nnl
Sampling	sml	ol	ol	ol	ol	ol	sml	ol	ol	cl
Totals	80	344	57	48	59	100	110	191	208	98
Ruff										
Black + Grey	44%	40%	19%	27%	20%	44%	31%	41%	29%	56%
Coloured	36%	52%	65%	65%	64%	32%	34%	33%	22%	30%
White	20%	8%	16%	8%	16%	24%	35%	26%	52%	14%

Key: G, Goethe; L, Lindemann; S, Shepard; D, Drenckhahn; H, Hogan-Warburg; R, Van Rhijn; sb, southern Belorussia (Pripet Marshes); nop, northeastern Poland; pom, Pommerellen (near Gdansk, Poland); est, Estonia; ns, northern Sweden; nwg, northern West Germany; nnl, northern Netherlands; sml, shot on migration or on lek; ol, observed on lek; cl, caught on lek.

Table 13 The percentages of light and dark ruffs in four samples of males observed around 1935 on leks in different areas by Lindemann.

		Light/White	Dark/Black	Totals
Southern Belorussia	52°N 27°E	23%	77%	344
Northeastern Poland	54°N 24°E	49%	51%	57
Pommerellen	54°N 18°E	25%	75%	48
Estonia	59°N 27°E	53%	47%	59

ably. For instance, Lindemann observed an increase from south (southern Belorussia) to north (Estonia) and from west (Pommerellen) to east (northeastern Poland) in the proportion of males with white or light-coloured ruffs in the population (Table 13). Camouflage was put forward as an explanation for these trends, because the probability of snow cover also varied in a similar way. Against this, Dobrinskij could not clearly establish such a phenomenon in populations from northern Siberia.

> Dobrinskij found that the proportion of light-coloured males (36%) in a sample collected in 1968 in Yamal (about 67°N, 70°E) was almost identical to the 34% found in a sample collected in the same year in Chanty-Mansijsk (about 61°N, 70°E). Similarly, the proportion of males with white ruffs (29% of 250 males) in a sample collected in 1967 in Taimyr (about 70°N, 85°E) was in the same range as in a sample (27% of 176 males) collected in the same year in Yamal. The proportion (48%) of 'melanic' males in the sample from Taimyr, however, was considerably lower than in the sample from Yamal (61%), but in the same range as in the samples from Yamal collected in 1965, 1966, and 1968 (47%, 47% and 43%).

Dobrinskij's data suggest a third factor, which may explain differences between samples: the composition of populations may *change from time to time*. Dobrinskij's sample size is probably sufficient to give an accurate description of the large populations in northern Siberia. This being so, it is hard to believe that the dramatic changes in the proportion of melanic males are a consequence of differential mortality or differential reproduction. I suggest that these fluctuations are due to the conditions in particular years, which may create the opportunity for certain sub-populations to migrate north to a greater or lesser extent. One might speculate that the differences between Goethe's sample and the big sample from Lindemann, both collected in southern Belorussia, were also caused by fluctuations between years. On the other hand, however, both samples originate from several years in succession in the same period (1930–1938). The possibility that the composition of the population has changed over time cannot be excluded, but this does not seem very likely in the comparison between Hogan-Warburg's sample (collected from 1960 to 1963 in the northern parts of the Netherlands) and my own sample collected from 1968 to 1971 in the same area.

There is a fourth factor which gives a more plausible explanation for the differences between Hogan-Warburg's sample and mine: the differences may be due to *sampling techniques*. Lidy Hogan-Warburg described all individuals visiting her leks. My sample was based on all individuals caught in snares on the leks. The likelihood of the various colour morphs occurring in a sample of males visiting a lek is probably different from that in snared males. In a sample of males visiting a lek, the resident males, who usually possess dark plumage types, are all included. Marginal males, possessing the same plumage types, only enter the sample if they visit the lek frequently enough. The number of satellite males in the sample, mainly males with white or light plumage types, depends on the observation intensity. Frequent observations on the same lek may describe all satellite males visiting the area, including all leks in the neighbourhood. Actually, this was Hogan-Warburg's sampling technique. A short observation session on the same lek reduces the proportion of satellite males in the sample, and might even miss all of them. In sampling males snared on a lek, satellites are under-represented because their unhurried pace is unsuitable for closing the snares around their feet. In a sample of males shot on leks, satellites and marginal males are under-represented because they do not have such strong bonds with the lek as the resident males. The latter tend to stay put when approached by humans.

The importance of the sampling technique also becomes apparent from data collected in the Netherlands on the proportion of males with white ruffs in flocks. On 21 April 1969 I observed two large foraging flocks close to the Lauwersmeer area. Out of 460 males in these flocks I saw only 32 (7%) with white ruffs. This is lower than the lowest proportion in Table 12. Even lower is my estimate of the proportion of males with white ruffs in 26 flying groups observed in April and May 1979 in the Lauwersmeer area. Out of 233 males in these groups I saw only nine (4%) with white ruffs!

Apart from the use of different criteria by the investigators for describing individuals, this fourth factor, different sampling techniques, seems to be a major cause of the high degree of variation between samples. Goethe's material was based on males shot in the breeding area, probably on leks. This may indicate that satellite and marginal males were under-represented. Lindemann's samples were based on descriptions of birds present on leks. His sampling technique is not clearly given, but, in view of the very low proportion of males with white ruffs, I guess that he only included territorial males. Shepard's sample is based on detailed descriptions of all males visiting a lek during a very short lekking season. Probably such a short season does not permit the satellites to switch between many leks and creates the impression of fewer satellites overall than in a long season. Drenckhahn's first sample was made up of males shot in northwestern Germany, probably partly on leks and partly in migrating groups. His second sample was based on observations on leks in the same area, aimed at the description of plumage types. His short observation sessions, once or a few times per lek, cannot have maximized the proportion of satellites. In Hogan-Warburg's sample, however, many extended observation sessions on the same lek during a very long season must have led to a very high representation of satellite males.

Summary

The nuptial plumage types of males are extremely diverse. Differences between various investigators in the description of these plumage types are mainly due to the use of different criteria and to different sampling techniques, but probably also to differences between geographical areas, and seasons. Variation occurs in colour and pattern of ruff and head-tufts, colour of wattles, legs, and bill, and darkness and shade of feathers on the back and the upper side of tail and wings. Some of these characteristics are interrelated. For instance, the colour of the ruff and head-tufts tend to be the same, especially when the pattern is regular with transverse striping. In contrast, plain or irregular patterned black ruffs are most often combined with coloured head-tufts, and plain or irregular patterned coloured ruffs are most often combined with black head-tufts. Other character-istics seem to vary independently of one another. For instance, the colour of the wattles around the bill and eyes is not related to the colour and pattern of ruff and head-tufts. The variation in plumage types between independent males differs from the variation in satellites. Plumage with any ruff and black head-tufts, namely independent plumage, only occurs in independent males. More than 50% of these males have such plumage. Plumage with a white ruff and head-tufts without any pattern in ruff, head-tufts or both, namely satellite plumage, only occurs in satellites, and is characteristic of roughly 50% of these. The other types of plumage, the atypical ones, may occur in both classes of male.

2.6 FEMALES ON LEKS

Females (reeves) can easily be distinguished from males (ruffs) by their smaller size, the lack of a ruff and head-tufts, and their behaviour. Sexual size dimorphism is considerable in this species. The body weight of an adult female is

Lek B near Roderwolde, end of May 1968. From left to right: preening female, Fireman and Yellow-face in the squat posture, male 12 with white satellite, both squatting, and standing female behind, Grandpa and Boss, both squatting.

only approximately 60% of the weight of an adult male. Wing length in adult females is always less than 175 mm, whereas all adult males have longer wings. During the breeding season females have, under all conditions, a slender neck, in contrast to the swollen neck of the males, which is conspicuous even during flight. Despite the lack of a ruff and head-tufts, there is some plumage polymorphism in females. They may have plumage in various shades of brown, and, additionally, have different kinds of patterns on the breast, such as small white bibs or bars on their feathers. Under ideal conditions one might be able to recognize individual females during more than one visit to the lek. The behaviour of females on the lek appears to be much more relaxed than that of males. Females may stand quietly on the lek for dozens of minutes, preen themselves extensively, and remain apparently untouched during fights and other interactions between males.

On 7 May 1968, lek B in Roderwolde was also visited by females (see Figure 7). During my observation session, lasting three hours, they spent altogether 95 minutes on the lek, which is only 1/18 of the total time spent by males. I counted nine visits by females during that morning; at most three females were present at the same time. During the major part of their attendance (53 minutes) the females did not stay very close to particular resident males. The remaining 42 minutes close to resident males were the result of 17 visits to residences. It may be surprising that only 33% of this time was spent with a resident male alone on his residence, and 67% with a resident male with one or two satellites.

Orange-face received the highest visiting rate of females, 19 minutes, all in company with one or two satellites. One female displayed intentions to crouch on his residence, but Orange-face did not get the opportunity to mate. Instead, the two satellites who were present on his residence at that time displayed such strong sexual arousal that they mounted each other, while performing copulation movements. Yellow-face was the second most preferred male, females spending 13 minutes on his residence, but, in contrast to Orange-face, for the major part of this time (10 minutes) he was unaccompanied by satellites. Bib got the company of a female for eight minutes, four minutes with a satellite and four minutes without. Boss and Grandpa each received a female for only one minute that morning.

Stay on leks

Females do not seem to be strongly attached to a particular lek. In Roderwolde I often saw them flying from lek A to lek B or vice versa. In 1971 I could see from the tower near lek D that females also moved between leks A and D. Leks can be further visited by females who do not seem to have any attachment to the area. In early spring in Roderwolde I frequently observed very large flocks of females, up to 200 individuals, which usually stayed in my study area for only one or a few days. Groups of up to 30 individuals visited the leks, and some females were even seen to copulate. By contrast, reports from several other investigators suggest that females are strongly attached to a specific lek or mating place.

Andersen, for instance, found approximately 15 nests km^{-2} within a 300 m radius of the lek, whereas the density further away was only about one fifth as great. Mildenberger and Khlebosolov even report very strong relationships between particular males, displaying alone or with a very small number of companions on small mating sites, and females nesting in their close vicinity.

Selection of a mate seems to be the main reason that females visit a lek. To choose the best partner, females should visit a lek with the maximum number of suitable mates. This possibility has been examined by correlating data on the percentage of time spent by females on various leks with the average numbers of resident, marginal, and satellite males on the same leks. Although there is a considerable amount of variation, all three comparisons show a distinct positive correlation, especially with regard to satellite numbers. Females do indeed tend to spend more time on leks with many males, especially satellites.

Females should also visit a lek *when* the maximum number of suitable mates is present. I investigated this possibility by comparing the changes in visiting rates of the various categories of individuals (see Figures 12 and 13). Females seem to display a flexible daily rhythm in lek visits which resembles that of satellites, but apparently differs somewhat from the more rigid daily rhythms of lek attendance by resident and marginal males. The visiting rate of females on a longer time-scale seems to be strongly related to the visiting rates of the different categories of males, especially resident males and satellites.

The relationships between female visits and visits of males to the lek can be illustrated by an analysis of 191 hours of observation on three leks near Roderwolde and the leks close to Boerakker, Gorredijk, Sebaldeburen, and Terwispel during the seasons 1969–1971 (Figure 18). For 36% of the time, I saw one or more females on the lek (horizontal broken line). Resident males spent

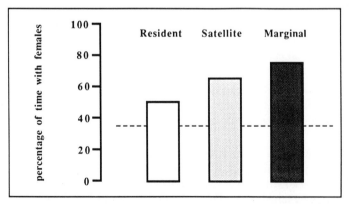

FIGURE 18 *The average percentage of time spent by resident males (R), satellites (S), and marginal males (M) together with females on the leks of Roderwolde, Boerakker, Sebaldeburen, Terwispel, and Gorredijk from 1969 to 1971. The average percentage of the observation time with females is indicated by a horizontal broken line.*

on average 50% of their time on the leks in company with females. If their presence were independent of female visits, they should spend only 36% of their time on leks in company with females. Thus, there exists a clear relationship between female visits to the leks and the visits of resident males. Satellite males spent on average 65% of their time on the leks in company with females. Thus, the relationship between female visits and satellite visits is even stronger than that between visits of females and of resident males. Marginal males spent on average 71% of their time on the leks in company with females, giving a still stronger correlation.

Arrival and departure on leks

Females often arrive singly, but may also arrive in a group with other females, or in a group with males. The relationships between female visits and the visits of males to the lek may arise in various ways, including a tendency to arrive and depart simultaneously with particular classes of birds, a preference for arriving when particular classes of birds are already present on the lek, and a tendency to postpone departure when particular classes of birds are still present on the lek. To investigate these possibilities I analysed all 1189 arriving groups, single birds included, and all 1133 departing groups of ruffs and/or reeves on lek B in Roderwolde during more than 74 hours of observation from 17 April to 5 June 1969. The tendencies of birds of a particular class to arrive or depart simultaneously with other classes can be deduced from the composition of the arriving and departing groups. Any tendency to arrive or depart when the other classes of birds are present or absent can be deduced from the composition of the group present on the lek.

The composition of the arriving groups (Table 14) was analysed by counting the number of times that, for instance, a resident male arrived together with one or more females (67 cases). To interpret the scores collected in this way, I had to compare them with the values which would be obtained if, continuing with the same example, resident males did not display a tendency to arrive together with or without females. That value (154) was calculated by multiplying the observed number of arrivals of individual resident males (820) by the probability that females were present in an arriving group. This probability was calculated by dividing the observed number of arriving groups with females (224) by the total number of arriving groups (1189). The large difference between the observed score (67) and the expected value (154) points to a tendency of resident males to avoid the company of females when on the way to a lek. The composition of the departing groups was analysed in a similar way.

The data presented in Table 14 suggest that resident males strongly avoid the company of females when arriving on a lek and when departing, that satellite males have a moderate tendency to arrive and depart together with females, and that marginal males have a strong tendency to arrive and depart with females. If one considers the reverse situation, the tendency of individual females to associate with groups containing the various classes of males, analogous trends

Table 14 Lek B, Roderwolde 1969: associations between females and the three classes of males in groups arriving on and departing from the lek.

	Class	I	G	Class	o	e	Class	o	e
Arrivals	R	820	478	R(f)	67	154	f(R)	38	110
	S	474	384	S(f)	123	89	f(S)	106	88
	M	729	477	M(f)	236	137	f(M)	157	110
	f	274	224						
	Total		1189						
Departures	R	781	518	R(f)	62	132	f(R)	32	125
	S	457	369	S(f)	129	77	f(S)	140	89
	M	707	436	M(f)	256	119	f(M)	197	105
	f	274	191						
	Total		1133						

Key: I, number of individuals; G, number of groups; o, observed number of individuals; e, expected number; R, resident males; S, satellite males; M, marginal males; f, females; (f/R/S/M), with f/R/S/M in group.
Note: groups may include more than one class of individuals, so the total number of groups is smaller than the sum of the numbers within each of the four classes.

can be observed. Females seem to very strongly avoid the company of resident males when arriving or departing, to display a slight tendency to arrive and depart together with satellites, and to display a fairly strong tendency to arrive and depart together with marginal males. Thus, these data give no clear answer to the question of whether the observed trends are caused by the behaviour of females, the behaviour of the various classes of males, or by the behaviour of females and males.

> The composition of the group present on the lek just before an arrival (Table 15) was analysed by counting the number of times that, for instance, a resident male arrived when one or more females was already present on the lek (24 cases). To interpret the scores collected in this way, I had to compare them with the values obtained if, continuing with the same example, resident males did not display a tendency to arrive when females were present or absent. That value (191) was calculated by multiplying the observed number of arrivals of individual resident males (820) with the probability that females were present on the lek. This probability was calculated by dividing the observed number of minutes with females on the lek (1039) by the total observation time (4465 minutes). The large difference between the observed score (24) and the expected value (191) points to a strong tendency of resident males to arrive on the lek during the absence of females. The composition of the groups staying on the lek after a departure was analysed in a similar way.

The data presented in Table 15 suggest that resident males display a very strong tendency to arrive and depart during the absence of females, that satellite males also (though to a lesser extent than resident males) tend to arrive and

Table 15 Lek B, Roderwolde 1969: conditions on the lek before arrival and after departure of females and the three classes of males.

Class	T	Class	o	e	Class	o	e
		Arrivals					
R	4333	R(f)	24	191·	f(R)	270	266
S	2188	S(f)	80	110	f(S)	153	134
M	1724	M(f)	219	169	f(M)	103	106
f	1039						
Total	4465						
		Departures					
		R(f)	15	182	f(R)	261	266
		S(f)	38	106	f(S)	174	134
		M(f)	156	164	f(M)	107	106

Key: T, number of minutes observed on lek (one or more individuals); o, observed number of individuals; e, expected number; R, resident males; S, satellite males; M, marginal males; f, females; (f/R/S/M), f/R/S/M on lek.

especially to depart during the absence of females, and that marginal males tend to arrive and depart when females are present on the lek. If one considers the reverse situation, the tendency of individual females to arrive or depart during the presence or absence of the various classes of males, the picture becomes somewhat different. Arrivals and departures of females seem hardly to be influenced by the presence of the various classes of males. Almost none of the observed scores differs from those expected. I only observed a slight tendency of females to depart during the presence of satellite males. I suspect that this phenomenon is not due to a particular property of females, but is caused by the property of satellites to stay during (and shortly after) the presence of females.

Thus, in combination with the finding that resident, satellite, and marginal males tend to stay on leks when females are also present (Figure 18), the data on arrivals and departures suggest that:

- *resident males* tend to arrive on the lek before the females are expected, and to depart when females are absent and unlikely to come to the lek;
- *satellite males* tend to arrive before or together with females and to depart together with females or after the females have left the lek;
- *marginal males* tend to arrive together with females or during the presence of females on the lek and depart mainly together with females;
- *females* mainly associate passively with the members of various classes of males on the lek, and, extrapolating from this, probably also with males in the arriving and departing groups.

The last suggestion does not imply that females do not actively take particular decisions. For instance, the decision of a female to go to a lek or to depart from a lek is clearly taken by herself. The daily and seasonal rhythm in the rate of visiting the lek by females (Figures 12 and 13) seems to be based mainly on the decision processes of females. The equivalent rhythms of the three classes of males seem to be caused by an anticipation of the female rhythm, mainly by resident and satellite males, and by direct responses, mainly by satellite and marginal males, to females flying in the neighbourhood of leks.

The most probable conclusion, that females influence the male's visiting rates to the lek, is wholly opposite to the ideas presented by Christoleit, one of the first investigators of the behaviour of Ruffs at leks. He believed that the communal display of males was designed to attract as many females as possible to the lek. For instance, the plumage polymorphism within the tight group of males was seen as an analogue of a multi-coloured flower bed with its strong power of attraction for honeybees and butterflies. He failed, however, to give any scientific support for these ideas.

Stay on residences

During visits to the lek, females may stay at the lek perimeter, position themselves somewhere between residences, or, just like satellites, select a site near to a particular resident male. Thus, resident males may get the company of females on the residences for part of their time. In my large sample of 191 observation hours on seven leks, a resident male was accompanied by one or more females on his residence for, on average, 6.6% of the time he spent on the lek, and by one or more satellite males for 16.0%.

Females spent 30–70% of their time outside the residences. However, they do not select a site on the lek to occupy at random. Certain resident males are more often visited than others. The tendency of females to visit particular residents may change in the course of a season.

> For instance, from 15 to 24 April 1968 on lek B, females spent most of their time on residences with Yellow-face and Boss. During the next 10 days from 25 April to 4 May, their preference for Yellow-face increased further. From 5 to 14 May, Orange-face became preferred, but Yellow-face still received a considerable proportion of the female visits. From 15 to 24 May, Boss, Grandpa and Yellow-face became the favoured hosts of the females. From 25 May to 3 June, females spent most time with Yellow-face and Fireman, and during the last period, from 4 to 13 June, with Yellow-face and Boss. These preferences differed from those displayed by the satellites (see p. 44), but also suggest some kind of overlap between both classes.

I studied the relationship between female and satellite visits to residences further, using data collected during roughly 35 early morning hours on lek B in the 1969 season. They comprise a very large number of samples, taken at intervals of one minute, of the number of females and satellites on every residence. Samples with both females and satellites present occur approximately three times as often as would have been expected if females and satellites

Table 16 Lek B, Roderwolde 1969: presence of females and satellite males on the residences.

A.	No satellites		Satellites present	
	o	e	o	e
No females	6052	5896	677	833
Females present	359	513	228	72

B.	No satellites		Satellites present	
	o	e	o	e
One female	290	263	140	167
More females	67	94	88	61

C.	One satellite		More satellites	
	o	e	o	e
No females	659	656	18	21
Females present	218	221	10	7

Key: o, observed number of cases; e, expected number of cases.

selected residences independently (Table 16A). This implies any combination of the following factors:

- females are attracted by satellites on a residence;
- satellites are attracted by females on a residence;
- females and satellites are both attracted by another property of some residences or resident males.

The first possibility is quite likely because the residences with satellites were visited relatively often by more than one female (Table 16B). The second possibility is less likely, because the presence of extra satellites does not seem to occur more often during the stay of females on a residence than during the absence of females (Table 16C).

Arrival and departure on residences

More direct information on the cause of the association between females and satellites was obtained from the movements of birds of both classes over the lek. If females, for instance, prefer to go to residences with satellites, the presence of the satellites must be considered as a cause, whereas the movement of females must be considered as an effect. Thus, to study the causal relationship, I had to take full account of all kinds of conditions during movements over the lek.

My watch on lek B on 24 April 1969 from 6.00 to 7.30 was specially planned to record these conditions. Altogether I observed 115 cases in which one or more females, satellites or individuals from both groups moved from one site to another on the lek. These cases included 82 moves by a female and 105 moves by a satellite. Table 17 shows how often different females or satellites moved

Table 17 Lek B, Roderwolde 24 April 1969: moves between residences by females and satellite males.

A.

| | Simultaneous moves to same residence | | | | | |
| | All data | | | Only two birds | | |
	s	o	e	s	o	e
Female + female	54	46	7.0	4	4	0.6
Satellite + satellite	21	6	2.9	14	5	2.1
Satellite + female	54	11	5.9	10	6	1.3

B.

| | Moves by females | | | | | |
| | All data | | | Single moves | | |
	n	o	e	n	o	e
	82			24		
Towards female(s)		16	9.0		2	1.8
Towards satellite(s)		26	16.0		7	3.7
Towards two satellites					3	0.6

C.

| | Moves by satellites | | | | | |
| | All data | | | Single moves | | |
	n	o	e	n	o	e
	105			49		
Towards female(s)		25	17.6		6	6.8
Towards satellite(s)		15	14.0		8	9.5

Key: s, simultaneous moves; n, total number of moves; o, observed number; e, expected number.

simultaneously to the same site on the lek (A), and how often females and satellites moved to a site with females, satellites or both (B and C). To understand the meaning of these observations, I calculated how often the different combinations should occur if individuals moved independently of one another. These expected values were primarily based on the number of visits by females and satellites to all different residences and to other preferred sites on the lek.

Table 17 clearly shows that individuals, especially females, tend to go to the same site on the lek, when they move at the same time (A). However, many of these moves were very complex, because more than two birds were involved. For this reason, one might doubt the possible conclusion that different individuals attract each other. To get around this difficulty, I separately analysed the simple cases in which only two females, two satellites, or one female and one satellite, moved from one site on the lek to another. Expected values were now calculated by adding the probabilities for all separate cases. One may infer from Table 17 that the trends are the same as in the complete set of data.

Table 17 further shows that females have a strong tendency to move to sites with other females or satellites (B), and that satellites do not tend to move to sites with females or other satellites (C). Here also, the simple cases, where only one female or one satellite moves, have been analysed separately. They show roughly the same trend. Thus, the attraction of females by satellites appears again to be more important than the reverse.

Summary

A female (reeve) is smaller than a male, behaves in a more relaxed manner on the lek, and has no ruff or head-tufts. Females are not strongly attached to leks. They prefer to visit leks with many males, especially those which are visited by many satellites. Fluctuations in female visiting rates to a particular lek are also positively correlated with fluctuations in male visiting rate. During arrival and departure, females are usually in company with marginal males, sometimes with satellites, and rarely with resident males. Resident males are usually present before the arrival of females and stay after the female's departure. Satellite males are frequently present before the arrival of females, and tend to stay after their departure. Marginal males usually arrive together with females or after their arrival, and frequently depart before the females leave the lek. Females seem to associate passively with the males. Thus, on the *scale of visits to a particular lek*, females seem to exercise a strong influence (cause) on the timing and rate of visiting by all categories of males. When present on the lek, females may stay alone, or associate with a resident male which may be accompanied by a satellite. Females display distinct preferences for particular residences. These preferences, which partly overlap with those displayed by satellites, may change during the course of the season. When selecting a residence, females tend to move together with other females or satellites towards residences with females or satellites. Thus on the *scale of visits to particular sites on the lek*, female visiting rate seems to be an *effect* of satellite visits.

2.7 MATING

When approaching a lek, or present on it, a female strongly influences the behaviour of the males. The males fight more frequently than in the absence of females. Resident males become less tolerant towards satellites visiting their residences. The behaviour of males divides more clearly into periods of excited movement by all individuals at the same time, and periods in which they all stay motionless for seconds, sometimes even for a minute or more. The presence of a female is also attended by particular behaviour patterns in the males, which do not occur when females are absent. This conspicuous pattern of behaviours, usually called *courtship*, and the transitions between motion and stillness, seem to stimulate females to crouch for a male and to accept mounting and copulation.

Most investigators, including myself, who have studied Ruffs in the breeding season, assume that the majority of courtship and almost all mating occurs on the lek. During my study I observed more than 500 copulations on leks, but not a single one outside the leks. I did observe courtship in foraging groups, but at a lower intensity than the courtship on leks. Nevertheless, the basis for assuming that courtship and mating normally occurs on leks is not very solid, because Ruffs are not easily watched elsewhere: they usually move away from an observer, having no attachment to any site. Consequently, the chance of seeing courtship and mating is relatively small. Despite several hundreds of hours close to leks, I only managed to watch the events in groups outside leks for one or a few hours. Other investigators have not managed much better, except for David Lank and Connie Smith who observed 17 off-lek matings in Finland, but still at much lower frequencies than on leks.

Some observers of leks have never seen even a single copulation and this is not exceptional. A review by Birkhead *et al.* shows that low copulation rates are very common among promiscuous birds. Sometimes I also watched a lek for several days, occasionally for more than a week, without seeing any copulations. However, this phenomenon has tempted some investigators, for instance Portielje and Lindemann, to claim that females rarely or never copulate on the lek, but instead go off with their preferred male to copulate elsewhere. I have no evidence for this view. On the contrary, males who are often visited by females on their residences usually stay after the female leaves. I am therefore convinced that the idea that females leave the lek for copulation after mate selection is sheer nonsense!

Approach of females to the lek

When moving more than a few dozen metres, ruffs usually fly, as do reeves when approaching a lek. The males on a lek seem to be very good at spotting flying conspecifics at distances of several hundred metres from the lek. When they see flying females, or, in some cases, also flying males, males on the lek orient towards them and perform a striking sequence of behaviour patterns, called the *reception ceremony*, which has been described in detail by Hogan-Warburg. Its main component is a short series of flapping movements with both wings, up and down at moderate speed, to display the white underside of the wings in a highly conspicuous way. Each burst of flapping lasts from one to two seconds and may be linked in long sequences by intervening pauses, lasting 0.5–1 second. During such flapping, the wings look like flashing lights. Usually many or all males on a lek (resident, satellite, and marginal males) join in this behaviour, resulting in a striking signal of their lek location to the approaching birds. The flapping movements may be made by a male from an erect posture, while standing or trampling with his feet on the ground. His tail may be spread, and the tail feathers may show a highly coordinated trembling movement. This standing variant of the reception ceremony is called *wing-fluttering* (Figure 19). Resident males usually stand on their residence during the performance, while satellite males normally position themselves between residences or, like marginal males, at the edge of the lek. In the variant called *flutter-jumping*, the reception ceremony may be combined with jumps from the ground using both legs simultaneously. The ceremony may even result in actual flight, in which the bird rises up to several metres above the lek. This final variant is called *hovering*.

Duration and structure of the reception ceremony seem to depend on the presence and previous visiting rates of females, and on the composition of the approaching group and its flight-path. When females are absent, ruffs tend to react more strongly to approaching groups than during their presence. Similarly, after a long absence of females, males seem to respond more strongly than after a short absence. Lidy Hogan-Warburg found that lek size also had an influence

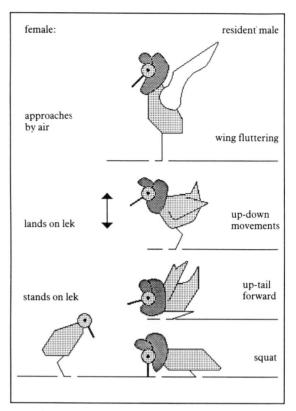

FIGURE 19 *The behaviour shown by males, especially resident males, during the approach and arrival of females on their lek.*

on the duration and structure of the reception ceremony. The strongest responses to approaching females were seen on the smallest leks. She suggested that the high level of aggression on large leks is the main cause of males on those leks showing a reduced tendency to perform the reception ceremony. I believe the distinction between small and large leks is primarily caused by differences in visiting rates of females. This is not necessarily contrary to Hogan-Warburg's suggestion that high visiting rates of females on large leks might influence the aggressiveness of the males on those leks.

I studied the effect of the presence of nearby females and satellites on the intensity of the reception ceremony by the various resident males. Satellites had a moderately depressive influence and females a very strong depressive influence.

The intensity of the reception ceremony of a particular male was measured by dividing the number of series of flapping movements of that male by the total duration of the

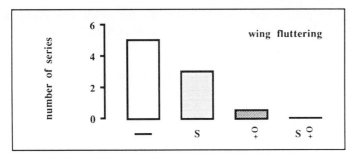

FIGURE 20 *The average number of flutter series of a resident male per 10 seconds of the reception ceremony of the group in four situations. —, no females or satellites on residence; S, only satellite(s) on residence; ♀, only female(s) on residence; S♀, satellite(s) + female(s) on residence.*

reception ceremony of the group. Males showed the strongest reactions (approximately one series of flapping movements per two seconds of ceremony) when there were no females or satellites on their residences (Figure 20). When they had only satellites on their residences the intensity dropped by about 30%, but when they had females on their residences they hardly showed any reaction to females arriving by air.

The strength of the response of males to approaching females further depends on the size of the approaching group, and on the proportion of males in such

Lek B near Roderwolde, 1967. Wing-fluttering: Fan-male in front on the right, and Orange-face just behind him.

groups. Large groups lead to strong responses, but purely male groups lead to weak ones. The reaction usually begins with wing-fluttering by one or a few males on the lek. Then, quite often, all, or most, other males look around, orient in the same direction as the birds who started the ceremony, and may take part in the display, especially when the approaching group is clearly visible and meets the conditions for a strong response (large with many females). When the group comes closer, the males on the lek may show flutter-jumping, especially when there are no females on the lek, and if females have not visited the lek very often recently. Flutter-jumping therefore seems to represent a stronger reaction than wing-fluttering. Hovering mainly occurs when a group with females does not immediately land on the lek, but turns, and seems to move away again. Hovering also occurs when the flight-path of a group is not clearly directed to the lek, a situation which might lead to the passing of the female or the group. Hovering seems to represent the strongest response, which is only displayed after a period of 'warming-up' with displays of lower intensity. If the approaching females do not land on the lek, some males, especially the marginal males, may leave the lek during hovering and follow the females. This suggests that the reception ceremony is partly caused by a tendency to follow females or other conspecifics. When a group passes, moves away from the lek, and gradually disappears from sight, hovering birds tend to conclude their reception ceremony with a few flutter-jumps and a short bout of wing-fluttering in which the up-and-down wing movements slow to an almost static display. Thereafter the resident males usually adopt the upright posture (Figure 14), and the satellites the tiptoe posture (Figure 16), both postures gradually changing into an oblique posture (Figures 14 and 16).

When approaching females land on the lek, the reception ceremony also stops, but much more suddenly. The resident males who were displaced during the ceremony immediately go to their residences and start to display very conspicuous *up–down movements* (Figure 19), while still oriented towards the approaching females. These movements are sequences of erect postures alternating every one or a few seconds with low postures (fully bent legs). The bill is held forward, or somewhat down. The tail may be spread and is tilted upwards. The wings are lifted to the side of the body. The up–down movements may be combined with *tail-trembling* and *bill-thrusting* but the frequency of moving up and down decreases quickly until the bird remains in a low posture, the *up-tail forward posture* (Figure 19). The tail is now held strikingly upwards and trembled in a highly coordinated manner. Up–down movements and the up-tail forward posture may also be shown by marginal males on the lek during the landing of females. Satellite males, however, do not show this behaviour but, in this context, quickly move from one residence towards another and select their position. When females finally stand on the lek all males sink into the squat posture (Figure 19) and freeze in that posture.

Alternation between immobility and sudden activity

Males on the lek remain immobile after females have landed for 10–100 s (on average 30 s). One of the resident males suddenly starts to move and this leads to a chain reaction by other resident males. Many of these perform a short series of movements, and then sink back into the squat posture. Activity during such interruptions of the motionless squat posture is sometimes shown from the half-squat posture (see Figure 16), which is combined with *turning* on a residence. This type of interruption is the prerogative of resident males without a satellite on their residence. During interruptions, resident males may also adopt the spread-tail forward posture (see Figure 17), directed at other males outside their residences or at the satellites present on their residences. The spread-tail forward posture, just like the half-squat posture, may be combined with turning, but also with bill-thrusting, charges and attacks directed at males outside the residence. When the spread-tail forward posture is aimed at satellites, it may be combined with bill-thrusting, pecking and attacks. In the presence of females the resident males continue, in synchrony, to alternate periods of immobility with short spells of vigorous movement. Immobile spells, lasting roughly 20 s, are associated with the squat posture, and, after a long presence of females, with the half-squat posture. Males sometimes remain for minutes in the squat posture, occasionally for the whole time during which the female is present. These males rarely fill the short interruptions of the squat posture with activity.

Together with two students, Tineke De Boer and Mechteld Leenknegt, I tried to trace the causes and effects of the short spells of activity which fill interruptions of the squat posture. First, I want to discuss the possible *causes* of these interruptions. One might imagine that they result from external factors, and to investigate this possibility I measured the duration of motionless squatting by resident males in four different situations (during the presence of females on the lek):

– without females or satellites on the residence;
– with one or more females on the residence, but without satellites;
– with one or more satellites on the residence, but without females;
– with both one or more females and one or more satellites on the residence.

My initial results, shown in Figure 21, suggested that satellites alone cause shorter squat durations than when satellites or females are absent; that females alone have a similar but less strong influence; and that the combination of females and satellites has an intermediate influence. Our later results were less clear-cut, although they confirmed that satellites alone cause the shortest squat durations, and also the highest frequency of short series of movements. They further showed that the frequency of short series of movements is lowest when females or satellites are absent from the residence.

The high frequency of short series of movements performed by resident males with satellites alone does not necessarily follow from a short squat duration. The males may

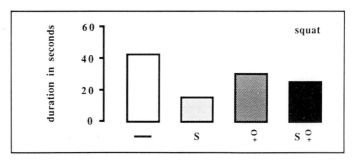

FIGURE 21 *The average duration of squatting by a resident male during the presence of females on the lek in four situations. Meaning of symbols as in Figure 20.*

show different tendencies in the four situations to resume squatting after an interruption. Our data showed that resident males with females, satellites, or both, on their residence maintained an immobile squat posture during approximately 90% of the time that their residences were visited, whereas resident males without females or satellites on their residences maintained the squat posture for only 30% of the time they stayed alone. Thus, satellites and females influence both the resident male's tendency to maintain squatting, and his tendency to indulge in short spells of activity.

We also studied whether the type of activity performed during the short series of movements was influenced by the presence of females on the residence. Two situations were compared: females present on the residence, and females present on the lek, but not yet on the residence. We scored the frequencies of movements performed from the half-squat posture (mainly turning), the frequencies of movements performed from the spread-tail forward posture (turning, bill-thrusting, pecking, attacking), and the frequencies of being the initiator of activity by more than one resident male. All types of activity were shown more often by the resident male during the presence of females on his residence than in the preceding period (i.e. after the arrival of females on the lek, but before the arrival of females on the residence).

I now want to discuss the *functions* of the interruptions during the squat posture. On Öland in Sweden, Julia Shepard found that reeves solicited copulations much more often from males with high display rates (and thus high frequencies of interruptions) than from males with low display rates. Although she did not show a direct relationship between female solicitation and display rate, her data suggest that display rate influences reproductive success. One of the basic requirements for reproduction in a resident male is the ability to attract females to his residence. Superficially it does not seem very likely that high display rates serve to attract females to residences. In that case one would expect high frequencies when females are on the lek, but not yet on the residence, and lower frequencies after the arrival of females on the residence. In fact we found the highest frequencies when females were on the residences. However, this comparison of frequencies is not a valid method of drawing conclusions about

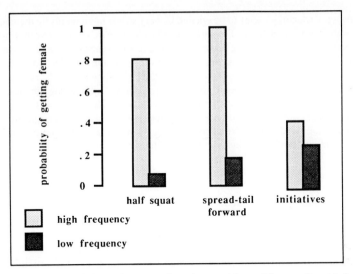

FIGURE 22 *The probability of getting females on his residence after high (light grey) and low (dark grey) frequencies of various types of behaviour by the resident male: movements performed in half-squat or spread-tail forward postures, and initiatives for communal activity by more males.*

function: definite answers can only be obtained from an analysis of the effect of the behaviour. Therefore we studied whether there was a relationship between the frequencies of these movements when females were not yet present on the residence, and the probability of attracting these females to the residence. We found, to our great surprise, that high frequencies of movements in half-squat and spread-tail forward postures, as well as initiatives for communal activity of males, all resulted in females visiting the residence more often than low frequencies of these movements (Figure 22). Thus, interrupting the squat posture with a short series of movements serves to attract females to the residence.

The high level of activity of a resident male during the presence of females on his residence suggests that the short series of movements has other functions, for instance to keep females for as long as possible, or to stimulate females to crouch. We investigated both possibilities, but could not find any evidence for them. In fact only negative relationships materialized. Males who took the initiative for communal activity, when accompanied by a female, lost such a female much faster than males who did not take the initiative while females were present on their residences. Females accompanying males who performed many movements from the spread-tail forward posture, crouched less frequently than females with males who made fewer movements. Yet crouching by a female always occurs after some kind of activity by the male in her immediate surroundings. Females never crouch for males who fail to interrupt squatting. Crouching seems to be elicited by very subtle movements by the male or by very subtle timing of them. For instance, Otto Von Frisch suggested that male and female interact by alternating between looking towards each other and looking away, comparable with the head-flagging display in the courtship of gulls. Looking away in both sexes was thought to be *caused* by the sexual unwillingness of the reeve. Looking away in the male was thought to have the *function* of making the female feel comfortable and to stimulate her sexual receptivity. The high level of activity of resident males during the presence of females on their residences might be a consequence of the need to move to elicit crouching. I strongly doubt whether such a high level of activity is of any direct advantage to the performer.

The advantage of having satellites

The main purpose of the interruptions during the squat posture seems to be to attract females to the residences. This conclusion offers a clue to the reason why females tend to visit residences on which the owner is accompanied by one or more satellites (p. 77). It is necessary to remember that satellites cause the shortest squat durations by resident males, and also the highest frequency of short series of movements by those males (see above). Thus, a satellite influences the resident male's behaviour by increasing his attractiveness to females. Of course, this does not exclude the possibility that the mere presence of satellites (or, for instance, the closeness of males) also attracts females. In that case the attractiveness to females of a double-occupied residence would be increased two-fold or more.

The finding that satellites raise the level of activity in resident males might suggest that the presence of satellites is no longer advantageous to the resident

Resident male in the half-squat posture (right) with squatting satellite (middle) and two standing females (left) (photo Joop Brinkkemper)

male after the arrival of a female on his residence. It would become more difficult for the resident male to stimulate females to crouch. Moreover, the resident male's chances of copulating with the female, should she crouch, would be reduced by the presence of a competitor. Indeed, all my data strongly suggest that a resident male does not profit by the presence of a satellite when his residence is frequently visited by females. The most important disadvantage seems to be that the resident male is almost unable to copulate when accompanied by a satellite. I found that only 13 out of 445 copulations by resident males were performed in the presence of satellites. This contrasts sharply with the proportion of time that resident males with females were also visited by satellites, 30–60%. Moreover, all 13 copulations during the presence of satellites occurred under unusual conditions. Ten of them took place on a lek which was recently established, and eight on residences with many females.

Resident males seem to avoid the difficulties of having both females and satellites in attendance by means of at least two mechanisms. Firstly, the resident males, who frequently copulate, are highly intolerant of satellites, often attacking them even when there are no females on the lek. These successful residents are rarely visited by satellites. Secondly, most resident males become intolerant of satellites during female visits to the lek, especially when these females visit their residences (Figure 23). During interruptions of the squat posture, they start to harass their satellites, initially by circling around them, adopting the spread-tail forward posture, and bill-thrusting and pecking at their wattles, and somewhat later by actual attacks, especially when females crouch on their residences. Most satellites move towards another residence after such treatment. Some satellites, however, may resist this harassment and seriously hinder the resident male's copulation activity, even to the extent of themselves succeeding in mounting the crouching female and inseminating her.

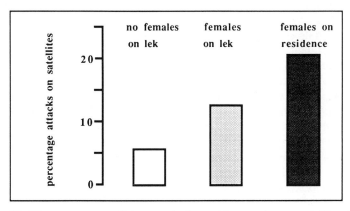

FIGURE 23 *The percentage of the attacks by resident males on satellites in three different situations.*

It may be concluded that the advantage to resident males of being accompanied by satellites remains restricted to the situation when no females visit the residence. Resident males behave towards satellites in a way that such an advantage is utilized, and the disadvantages minimized. The resident males tolerate, perhaps even attract, satellites when they are rarely visited by females. When the females have found the way to their residences, however, tolerance of satellites gives way to intolerance. When, after a week or so, females lose interest in these resident males, the latter may once again tolerate the presence of satellites.

Fighting

While females are present, resident males not only show an increased tendency to attack satellites, but also attack other resident males much more often. Strangely enough, marginal males do not receive more attacks from resident males during the presence of females. Lidy Hogan-Warburg proposed that the increased fighting activity occurred especially on small leks; fighting for territories on large leks would mainly occur during the absence of females. I could find no evidence for this suggestion. On leks of all sizes the resident males attacked other males more often when females were present than when they were absent. The frequency of fighting did vary between leks, but there was no relationship with the number of resident males on those leks. Similarly, the attack rate on the three classes of males, resident, satellite, and marginal, was not related to lek size. Thus, the risk of becoming the victim of an attack does not increase on larger leks, whether for resident males, for satellites, or for marginal males.

Lidy Hogan-Warburg believed that females were frightened by fighting males and would tend to leave the lek when fights were in progress, not an advantageous situation for males. I did indeed observe that females tended to withdraw from fighting males on the lek, but also noticed that resident males who launched short charges or attacks on neighbouring males frequently elicited crouching in females on their residences. Such residents may copulate as soon as they return from an attack. It sometimes happens, however, that the crouching female is mounted and inseminated by a satellite male during the brief attacks by his host, especially when the satellite is present on the same residence. In fact almost all copulations by satellites occur during very short absences of their hosts, usually when they attack other birds.

It may be that fighting establishes a dominance hierarchy. The highest-ranked males would get most copulations, either by fixing a rule about the right to copulate, or through a real preference of females for males with the best fighting abilities. To look at this I analysed over 1000 attacks by the resident males in 1969 on lek B in Roderwolde. In this large sample the copulation frequencies of the males were not correlated with the frequency of fighting, nor with the proportion of fights initiated. Thus, a dominance hierarchy does not seem to exist.

It is much more likely that fighting serves to establish a rule about the exclusive rights to a specific territory, or residence. This follows from the occurrence of take-overs of residences after serious fights, and from the high number of fights involving newly settled males. Should such rights not be clearly established, resident males may be troubled with interference by other resident males during or even before copulation. Short attacks during the presence of a female may serve to affirm these rules, and thus to lower the probability of interference by neighbours. Satellites therefore seem to have the best chance of copulation on the residences of males who have not fully established their exclusive rights and need to affirm them before they can copulate without interference from other residents. In other words, the high frequency of fighting during the presence of females is certainly not a disadvantageous trait in the Ruff, but seems to be required to ensure undisturbed copulation.

Courtship and mate selection

After the arrival of females on a lek, all or almost all males adopt the squat posture. Females usually adopt a *long-neck posture* just after their arrival, and again before departure. Apparently it signals a tendency to fly away. While the males remain immobile, the long-neck posture changes into a *short-neck posture*. The immobility of the males seems to make the females comfortable. Under these conditions females may start to walk quietly over the lek, possibly looking for a place to stay, or to select a mating partner. Females may show long bouts of preening during the periods of male immobility, or even adopt the *dropped-wing posture*. The latter posture mostly precedes crouching, and thus seems to express sexual receptivity. Females may also show *feather-touching*, a movement of the bill towards the plumage of a squatting male, especially his ruff. This behaviour has been explained by Lindemann as signalling a definite choice of a mating partner by the female. However, there is no evidence at all for this idea. Lindemann rarely observed copulation and believed that the female disappeared with her partner to copulate undisturbed away from the lek. I have the impression that feather-touching is not associated with sexual receptivity: it is rarely combined with the dropped-wing posture, and it almost never precedes crouching.

Although females may display almost any behaviour while males squat immobile, the males are unable to persuade them to crouch by squatting alone. Females are attracted to particular residences, or are stimulated to crouch by male behaviour occurring during interruptions of the squat posture, or after its termination. The patterns shown by resident males during these interruptions have been discussed already, namely the half-squat posture (with turning) and the spread-tail forward posture (with turning, bill thrusting, pecking and attacking). Satellite males may rise during squatting to the half-squat posture. This posture may be combined with turning. On residences with females, rising provokes severe pecking and attacks by the resident owner. Quite often the

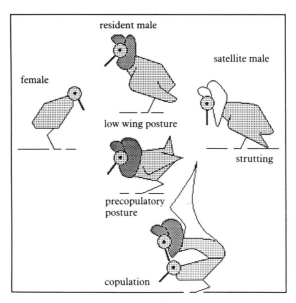

FIGURE 24   *Courtship and copulation postures.*

resident male squats with his bill on the head of the satellite. As soon as the satellite starts to move, the resident male reacts aggressively. As a result the satellite immediately sinks back into the squat posture, or moves, while adopting the *tiptoe posture*, to another residence or to the margin of the lek. On a residence without females nearby, rising of the satellite also elicits aggressive behaviour in the resident male, but less vigorously.

After the squat posture, a resident male may adopt the half-squat posture, which may change into the *low-wing posture* (Figure 24), especially when the male is not accompanied by a satellite, and when the females are not nearby. In this posture the male turns and orients both sides alternately towards the female, and may then show one- or two-sided *wing-lifting*, displaying the white underside of the wing to the female. Wing-lifting causes a flashing effect, lower in frequency than during the reception ceremony. Resident males may also terminate the squat posture with the *precopulatory posture* (Figure 24), especially when there are crouching females nearby. In that posture the male turns towards the female to get into a position to mount. If the female does not turn away, the precopulatory posture is usually followed by mounting and copulation (Figure 24). Cloacal contact occurs for only a few seconds. After a successful copulation, the female usually performs *wing-flapping*, in which both wings are quickly flapped up and down a few times. After both unsuccessful and successful copulations, the female may preen. Females may copulate more than once during the same visit, but rarely more than three times.

While females are present, marginal males may also show some courtship behaviour. Some of them squat after the arrival of females, but many maintain an upright or oblique posture at the border of the lek. A marginal male who has entered an empty residence, however, does squat during the presence of females. Sometimes a marginal male approaches a satellite who is standing at the side of the lek. These birds may form a twosome and squat together somewhere aside from the lek, especially when there are females nearby. Marginal males may interrupt the squat posture during the short periods of activity by resident males. They may then behave like resident males, but less frequently. After the squat posture, marginal males may also show the low-wing posture combined with wing-lifting. I have, on rare occasions, seen a marginal male approach a female in a precopulatory posture, but only beside or away from the lek. The same posture, however, was frequently shown by the so-called naked-nape males, just before homosexual copulations. I have occasionally seen females crouch in the neighbourhood of marginal males, but they never go on to copulate.

After the squat posture, a satellite male may raise himself into the *strutting posture* (Figure 24), and walk slowly towards the female, though rarely in the presence of the resident male. It is seen most often when the owner has left his residence to charge or attack another male. Females may crouch in response to the strutting display. Satellites may also rise from the squat posture and try to mount and copulate with the resident male or another satellite male on the same residence. This especially happens when females are nearby but tending not to crouch very often. Resident males may display the same behaviour towards satellites on their residences. Satellite males react very rapidly to a crouching female, and rise, approach her, mount and copulate (Figure 24) within a couple of seconds.

Copulation attempts by both resident and satellite males may be disturbed by other males on the lek. Residents may vigorously attack satellite males when they try to copulate, as well as copulating neighbours. Successful copulation rarely follows such attacks. Usually the female becomes scared and leaves the residence. Interventions by satellites are not generally aggressive. Satellites simply try to push the other male from the female's back and to copulate in his place. Satellites may thus intervene successfully, but may also merely mount the copulating male and try to copulate on his back.

Edmond Selous observed a considerable number of copulations on the famous lek on Texel. He realized that these copulations were performed by only a small minority of the males present on the lek, and thought the successful males were also the most beautiful. He considered this a very clear example of Charles Darwin's principle of sexual selection. His description now seems too simple, and not in line with our present knowledge of population genetics. If females only selected certain particular plumage types, the considerable degree of polymorphism among males would rapidly decline. Yet, while investigators do agree that females select particular males, nobody is certain about all the

Lek B near Roderwolde, end of May 1968. From left to right: Yellow-face and male 12 both in the up-tail forward posture, Grandpa in the squat posture with standing female, strutting white satellite, and Boss in the squat posture.

criteria they use. Successful males generally possess well-developed plumage, are experienced and, as far as resident males are concerned, defend a central residence on the lek. All these factors suggest that age is important. It is to the advantage of the female to select older males which have proved capable of survival, and so should pass on good genetic traits to her offspring. However, this has nothing to do with Darwin's concept of sexual selection and would neither lead to marked sexual dimorphism in plumage, nor influence the variation in plumage patterns between males. Besides age, there must be other factors which play a role in mate selection, since several older males were not very successful in getting copulations. For instance, Fan-male and Orange-face were fairly old in 1968 and 1969, but got almost no copulations. Neither was Bib successful, despite spending no less than five successive seasons on lek B. Some males may be favoured by the females year after year, for instance Boss in 1967 on lek A, and in 1968 and 1969 on lek B. Other males, for instance Grandpa on lek B, suddenly lose their favourite position. All my attempts to identify any other criteria for mate selection failed. I tried to relate numerous male characters to copulation frequency, but without success. Although the concept of sexual selection explains the excessive dimorphism between males and females, it is impossible to prove that it works through the behaviour shown on the lek.

Summary

Most courtship and mating occurs on the leks. Reeves approaching a lek elicit a conspicuous wing-flutter display in males, the reception ceremony. The male's response is strongest if female visits are rare, when females are not yet present, and when the approaching group is large. When the reeves land on the lek, the ruffs respond with a short series of displays. Thereafter they freeze in a squatting posture. Whilst a female is nearby, a male may interrupt fairly long periods of immobility with a short series of movements. Most often the alternation between immobility and activity is shown by different males at the same time. The proximity of satellites increases the tendency of resident males to interrupt immobility. The proximity of females increases the frequency of movements shown during spells of activity. The main function of the explosions of male activity is the attraction of females to residences. Crouching is stimulated by more subtle movements of the male. The advantage to resident males of being accompanied by satellites is restricted to the situation when no females are nearby. Intolerance towards satellites is shown during the presence of females on their residences, and during periods with high female visiting rates. The proximity of females also increases the frequency of fighting among resident males. This sometimes frightens the females, but may also cause them to crouch. Satellite males may copulate during attacks by hosts on neighbours. Fighting seems to have the function of fixing a rule about the exclusive rights to a specific residence. Courtship and mate selection include a number of characteristic displays. Females seem to prefer males with well-developed plumage on central residences on the lek. These are mainly old males. Preferences for particular plumage types have not been demonstrated.

2.8 ALTERNATIVE MALE STRATEGIES

Alternative reproductive patterns in males, comparable to the distinction between satellites and independent males in the Ruff, have been found in a wide variety of animals. In such species a clear distinction can be made between males who achieve reproductive success by aggressive behaviour towards other males, and males who behave submissively but still succeed in breeding.

One way in which submissive males can reproduce is by taking advantage of any short periods *when dominants lose control over their females*, such as when aggressive encounters occur amongst dominants. For example, Tim Clutton-Brock and his associates have found that, while two Red Deer stags fight, a submissive stag may sneak into the harem of one of the dominants and copulate. In Red Deer (*Cervus elaphus*), and in many other species, these 'sneakers' are usually the younger, weaker individuals. Sneakers may become dominants later in life. The profitability of the sneaking strategy is mostly low: 'sneakers' seem to make the best of a temporarily bad job.

Submissive males, behaving inconspicuously, may also *intercept females*, who are attracted by courting dominants. This kind of behaviour has frequently been observed among species in which females respond to the vocal signals of males, such as crickets and frogs. The dominant males call, and usually disperse in response to each other's sounds. Nearby callers may attack one another. The submissive males remain silent, quite often in the close vicinity of vocalizing dominants, so as to meet females approaching a vocalizing dominant. William Cade has shown that the singing behaviour of Field Crickets (*Gryllus integer*) depends on a number of factors, including male density and genetic constitution. At low densities almost all males sing and behave aggressively towards neighbouring singers. At high densities some of the males adopt the silent strategy, suggesting that these two roles are interchangeable. However, Cade's finding, that singing rate can be influenced by a few generations of artificial selection, shows that particular genotypes are pre-adapted to adopt either the silent or the singing strategy.

In frogs and toads, vocalization usually occurs in aggregations, comparable to leks, and the older larger males croak especially from the central positions. Each of these males maintains a small temporary territory, on which no other males are tolerated. Younger, smaller males stay at the periphery of the group. Under particular conditions these subordinate males may intrude into the chorus, but without calling. For instance, in the Bullfrog (*Rana catesbeiana*), Steve Emlen found that during nights with many females present some small males moved into the chorus in a posture in which vocalizing was not possible. Such males, who do not suffer aggression from the established males as long as they remain silent, seem to be able to take part in reproduction. It is very unlikely, however, that these silent frogs are as successful as callers.

In several animal species, submissive males may reproduce by *mimicking females and deceiving the dominants*. In many cases this seems to be associated with special evolutionary adaptations. Submissive males approach dominants who are courting females, and may steal fertilizations when the female is ready to accept copulation, or, more commonly in the case of external fertilization, when the female lays her eggs. The silent Bullfrogs may, because of their postures, mimic females. There are numerous other examples. In both Ten-spined Sticklebacks (*Pygosteus pungitius*) and Three-spined Sticklebacks (*Gasterosteus aculeatus*), Desmond Morris and Hans van den Assem found that territorial males may sneak into neighbouring territories while a female is spawning. They seem able to fertilize the new clutch of eggs before the male selected by the female has the opportunity to creep through the nest. Such sneaking males lose their nuptial colours and acquire the appearance of a female. Sticklebacks who adopt the sneaky strategy also have a nest and also try to attract ripe females to their territories, and so may easily switch strategies. It is difficult to estimate the success of the sneaky strategy in comparison with the conventional strategy, but it seems as if sneaking is most often used by males who are not very successful in attracting females to their territories. Thus, in sticklebacks also, sneaking seems to be a pattern evolved to make the best of a bad job.

Role switching is less common in many other species of fish. In the Mediterranean species *Tripterygion tripteronotus*, Peter Wirtz and Jolanda de Jonge found that large males defend territories with at least one small hole in the rocks for collecting eggs. Females deposit their eggs only in these territories. The territorial males possess conspicuous nuptial colours, guard the eggs, aerate the water in the holes by fanning, and take care of the young. Smaller males, who look like females, enter these territories during spawning of a female and try to fertilize the eggs. Female mimics possess special properties which contribute to the success of their strategy. For instance, their testes comprise about 4% of the body-weight compared with only 2% in territorial males. Thus, if role-switching occurred in these species, it would have to be associated with considerable physiological changes, a remote possibility. Role-switching is even more unlikely in the Bluegill Sunfish (*Lepomis macrochirus*), studied by Wallace Dominey in Lake Cazenovia, New York. In this species also, the larger males defend nesting territories in densely packed colonies. Territorial males can easily be distinguished from females by their colour pattern, while the smaller female mimics can hardly be distinguished from females. As in *Tripterygion*, female mimics have relatively larger testes than territorial males. It is unlikely that these two roles represent different developmental stages, because the age distributions of both types of males are almost the same. Thus, there are strong indications in this species that the status of a male (territorial or female mimic) is constant throughout life. In such a system the status of an individual might be determined by external factors during early development. Alternatively, or additionally, genetic factors might play a role. If the strategy of an individual is predetermined by its genes, and the successes of the various strategies are the same, then the proportions of individuals adopting the various strategies would be constant.

Submissive males may also get the chance of breeding in exchange for rendering *assistance to the dominants*. For instance, Peter Wirtz found that in Kenyan Waterbuck (*Kobus ellipsiprymnus*) some of the territorial males tolerate an additional adult male. These extra males participate in the defence of the territory and may obtain a small proportion of the copulations. Although they get fewer copulations than the territorial males, they seem to be more successful than the males who do not have access to a territory. The main advantage of associating with a territorial Waterbuck, however, is a considerable increase in the chance of becoming the new territory owner. The immediate benefit of associating with a territorial male is fairly low, but increases on a longer timescale if the associate inherits the territory. Similar social systems, in which submissive males may reproduce in exchange for helping dominants, have also been found among primates, for instance in the colony of Chimpanzees (*Pan troglodytes*) described by Frans de Waal. However, the relationship between helping the dominant and getting a share in the opportunity to reproduce is probably not causal. It seems unlikely that both the dominant and the subordinate assess the costs and benefits of the various possibilities, and then negotiate the best solution for both. Such a relationship must be the consequence of a lengthy evolutionary process.

It is only a small step from social systems in which dominant males are assisted by subordinates in maintaining a territory or a high status, to systems in which breeding pairs enlist other (related or unrelated) conspecifics, called helpers, to help take care of the offspring. Helping is not necessarily associated with an immediate return, such as a share in the copulations. On a longer time-scale, however, helping can be beneficial because it may increase the chances of acquiring a mate, a nest-site, or a territory, and thus the probability of reproducing in the future. Remarkable cases of helping are known from birds. The long-term benefits of helping non-family members have, for instance, been demonstrated in the Pied Kingfisher, studied in East Africa by Uli Reyer, and in the White-fronted Bee-eater, studied by Steve Emlen.

The strategies in the Ruff

In the Ruff the resident males control the mating sites, excluding marginal males from them. Consequently, marginal males lack mating opportunities unless they succeed in occupying a residence and achieving resident status. Role-switching occurs frequently between these two groups of males, and so the precise role of an independent male seems to be associated with age, physical strength, and, of course, with ownership of a territory.

If one assumes that almost all copulation occurs on leks, satellite males depend on the territory owners for reproduction. Likewise, resident males depend on satellites for the attraction of females to their residences. The tolerance of resident males seems to be due to an evolutionary process guided by the preference of females for residences occupied by two males. Thus, a satellite seems to become accepted on a territory in exchange for assisting the resident male in luring females to his territory.

The proximate factors leading to tolerance of satellite males by residents are probably the special features of satellite behaviour, which seem to inhibit the aggression of resident males. A satellite may be recognized as a male because of its size and nuptial plumage. Its behaviour, however, strongly resembles a female's, especially when only males are present on the lek, thus constituting a kind of deception of the resident males. Lidy Hogan-Warburg called it a *behavioural trap* in which a resident male is unwittingly caught. The so-called naked-nape males create an even more efficient trap. Their sex is advertised neither by plumage, nor by behaviour; only their size is a reliable indication of masculinity.

There is no evidence that resident males intentionally allow satellites to copulate on their residences. That satellites do copulate on these places is mainly, or completely, because resident males sometimes lose control over the females present on their territories. This usually happens during attacks on neighbours, but it may also occur when many females simultaneously visit the same residence. The copulation frequency of a satellite on a particular residence therefore depends on the amount of control of the owner over the females and also on the ability of the satellite to exploit periods when the owner loses control.

An additional factor enabling satellites to copulate is their ability to respond quickly to females who apparently crouch for the resident male. Satellite males can mount and copulate with such females before the resident male is ready, so constituting the kind of interception strategy shown by the crickets and frogs discussed previously.

Hence, all the features of the alternative strategies seen in other species (assistance to dominants, deception of dominants, lack of control over females by dominants, and the interception of females) are also observed in satellite males in the Ruff. Some of these can be associated with the tolerant behaviour of resident males towards satellites (assistance to dominants and deception of dominants). The others relate to the copulation behaviour of satellites (lack of control over females by dominants and interception of females).

Reproductive success

Since Edmond Selous' observations on Texel, the existence of two male strategies in the Ruff has been recognized. Both strategies seem to occur in all areas where the behaviour of Ruffs has been studied: the Netherlands, Denmark, Scandinavia, East and West Germany, Poland, Finland, and even northern Siberia. This universal similarity suggests that both the independent and the satellite strategies are viable. However, while the satellites, being the sub-dominant males, may be merely making the best of a bad job, it is also possible that both strategies enjoy approximately the same reproductive success. If that were the case, an important condition for the genetic control of status would be met. A comparison of the reproductive success of both strategies would clarify this point.

For the most reliable comparison one has to know the average number of reproducing offspring produced by a satellite and an independent male. However, our knowledge about the contributions of both types of male to the next generation rarely extends beyond their relative numbers of copulations. The males seldom maintain bonds with the females inseminated by them (some fieldworkers, especially Mildenberger and Khlebosolov, present an alternative view), and the females mostly disperse after copulation. The situation becomes even more complicated, since females may copulate several times, and also with more than one male. In some cases one can observe actual cloacal contact, but for the rest the success of copulation remains obscure. Thus, copulations, ideally cloacal contacts, or even more ideally inseminations, are the only means for estimating reproductive success. It is unknown whether all, or almost all, copulation occurs on leks, as it is practically impossible to observe it elsewhere. I remain undecided regarding the relative importance of copulations outside leks, and how such copulations might be distributed between satellites and independent males. The only relevant observations are from Lank and Smith in Finland: one off-lek mating by a satellite and 16 by independent males. Thus, my best estimate of reproductive success of satellite and independent males will be based on a subset of the copulations: those performed on leks.

It is quite easy to score the copulations made by satellites and by independent males on a lek. One can also easily calculate the average number of copulations per resident male per unit time, because these males remain on the lek almost all day. However, it is difficult to calculate the average number of copulations per independent male per unit time, since one must include marginal males, who do not spend so much time on leks and may visit various leks on the same day. For this reason the total number of marginal males visiting the lek per season or per day is not a very good measure. I prefer to express the copulation frequency of independent males as copulations per male-minute spent on the lek. Satellite males may also visit various leks on the same day and their copulation frequency was expressed in the same way. From 1969 to 1972 the observations which could be used for these calculations included 191 copulations by resident males, none by marginal males, and 28 by satellite males. These copulations occurred during 71 107 male-minutes spent by resident males, 11 928 male-minutes spent by marginal males, and 12 396 male-minutes spent by satellite males. Thus, on average, a resident male copulated 0.0027 times per minute spent on the lek, a marginal male zero times per minute, an independent male 0.0023 times per minute, and a satellite male 0.0023 times per minute, precisely the same frequency as an independent male!

Of course, I cannot pretend that these estimates are directly related to reproductive success. A copulation does not necessarily lead to surviving offspring. Moreover, the outcome of a copulation may be different for satellites and independent males. Satellite males, for instance, usually copulate very quickly. Hence, the probability of sperm transfer, or the amount of sperm transferred, may be lower in copulations by satellites than in copulations by independent males. The success of a copulation may also be related to its timing. Copulations performed early in the season may be more successful than copulations at the end of the season. This would benefit satellites, since they tend to copulate somewhat earlier in the season than independent males. A resident male also spends considerably more time on a lek than either a marginal male or a satellite. This means that the number of male-minutes recorded for a particular class of males is not directly related to the frequency of that class in the population. It also means that marginal males and satellites may have more chances of copulating outside leks than resident males.

In spite of all these objections, I was very surprised that the estimated copulation frequencies for independent and satellite males were precisely the same! This implies that the differences between the two strategies may in fact be controlled by genetic factors and that the two behaviours coexist with an equal likelihood of reproductive success.

Genetic control

Role switching between satellite and independent males is very rare, and seems to be incomplete when it does occur. All individuals who could be traced over more than one breeding season displayed a remarkable constancy in their roles. This was observed not only in the field but also in a group of Ruffs held in a large aviary. The few temporary changes of roles which were observed occurred under extreme conditions, such as during a long absence of the regular host, or separation from other males. This strongly suggests that the role of a male is determined early in life. Two types of determinants are involved in early fixation of the role: genetic and environmental factors.

The question of whether a character displayed by some individuals in a population is due to genetic factors may be tackled by a comparison between parents and offspring. For the status in males living in natural conditions it would be extremely difficult to perform such an analysis, considering the Ruff's mating system and the fact that status cannot be determined before the age of one year. Such an analysis would only be feasible using birds living under artificially controlled conditions. Mainly for this reason a small population of Ruffs was maintained at the Zoology Department in Groningen (see Section 2.3). To be certain of paternity, breeding groups were composed of a small number of females and a single male. Unfortunately, reproduction was very poor in these groups and only two males with known fathers were raised until their status could be determined. One of them, which developed light-coloured plumage, appeared to display satellite behaviour. The other one, which grew fairly dark plumage, started to display the behaviour of an independent male. The first male was the son of a white satellite, and the second was the son of a black resident male. Although this result agrees with the hypothesis of genetic control, it does not prove the case, because the sample size is so small. A dark male raised by David Lank and Connie Smith further supports the hypothesis. This bird behaved as an independent male and was the son of an independent male of strongly matching plumage.

Until now, direct evidence for the genetic control of status in the Ruff has been lacking. However, there are some indirect clues which strongly suggest an influence of genes. First of all, of course, there are analogous cases in which the influence of genes has been demonstrated. William Cade has shown that the difference between singers and non-singers in the Field Cricket (p. 94) partly rests on genes, because artificial selection on calling rate leads to a very clear response within a few generations. Similarly, differences in aggression between the tan and white colour morphs of the White-throated Sparrow, described by Falls and Ficken *et al.*, seem to be due to chromosomal differences between the two morphs.

Second, as I described earlier, there is a clear relationship between status and plumage (see Section 2.5). Certain plumage types, called satellite plumage types, have only been observed in satellite males. These comprise the following: a plain white ruff with plain white head-tufts, a plain white ruff with patterned white head-tufts, and a patterned white ruff with plain white head-tufts. Certain other plumage types, called independent plumage types, have only been observed in independent males. These comprise all types with black head-tufts and any colour of the ruff, black and white included. The remaining types of plumage, called atypical plumage types, have been observed in both groups of males. In the sample of 214 males described by Lidy Hogan-Warburg, 17% showed satellite plumage types, being 44% of the complete group of satellites. Thus, 56% of the satellites had atypical plumage types. The proportion of independent plumage types was 36% in the same sample. This comprised 47% of the independent males.

Direct evidence that the variation in plumage is under genetic control is as scarce as that for the genetic control of status. However, a study by Amelia Segre and co-workers indicates that isozyme variability in the Ruff is considerable. This implies that genetic variation is also considerable, and thus that there might be a genetic effect controlling plumage variation. Yet, variation in the blood serum proteins was not directly connected with plumage variation. In many analogous cases, however, genetic control of plumage variability has been clearly demonstrated. For instance, Peter O'Donald and his associates have shown that variation in colour phases in the Arctic Skua is based on a genetic polymorphism. A similar phenomenon has also been demonstrated in the Lesser Snow Goose by Fred Cooke and his colleagues.

The strong relationship between status and plumage suggests that both properties are under the control of the same genes. The clear division into three plumage types, satellite, independent, and atypical, could imply that three different genotypes are involved. In that case the satellite plumage types would most probably represent a homozygous combination of a particular allele, the independent plumage types a homozygous combination of two alternative alleles of the same gene, and the atypical plumage types a heterozygous combination of the two types of allele. Assuming that natural selection does not work to the advantage of one of these genotypes, and further that all genotypes randomly spread through the population, there should exist a special relationship between the frequencies of the three types. This relationship is known among population geneticists as the Hardy-Weinberg equilibrium. To test whether this equilibrium exists, I analysed the numbers of individuals with the three plumage types in the data presented by Lidy Hogan-Warburg (Table 18). In the whole sample of 214 males, 35% of the individuals had independent plumage types, 48% atypical plumage types, and 17% satellite plumage types, very close indeed to the proportions predicted by the Hardy-Weinberg rule. The expected frequencies in the four sub-populations were also only slightly different from the observed numbers. Thus, there is no reason to reject the idea of three genotypes controlling status and some aspects of plumage.

Table 18 The analysis of the frequencies of the three plumage types, based on the descriptions of males by Hogan-Warburg in four sub-populations of the Ruff in the northern part of the Netherlands from 1960 to 1963.

	Independent		Atypical		Satellite		
	o	e	o	e	o	e	Totals
Whole sample	76	75.3	102	103.4	36	35.3	214
Sub-samples:							
Schiermonnikoog	11	11.3	16	15.5	5	5.3	32
Roderwolde	9	14.2	21	19.3	10	6.6	40
Hasselt	26	25.3	36	34.8	10	11.9	72
Oosterwolde Polder	30	24.7	29	33.8	11	11.6	70

Key: o, observed number of males; e, expected number according to the Hardy-Weinberg law.

Control of behaviour by plumage

In view of the strong relationship between status and plumage, male behaviour might be explained by a direct influence of plumage on status, independently of the genes. Light males would rarely show aggression, but dark males would show it frequently. Various mechanisms for such an influence could be imagined. For instance, the behaviour of a male could arise from a comparison by that particular male between its own plumage and the plumage of other males on the same lek. Aggression would be inhibited in an environment of dark males, but facilitated in an environment of light males. It could also be possible that the behaviour of a male is moulded by the reactions to his plumage by other males: intolerant if he is dark, or tolerant if he is light.

These suggestions may be tested by artificially changing plumage colours. This method has been applied by Amelia Segre on captive males in the Zoological Park in New York, and also, on a much smaller scale, by myself in the field.

In the New York Zoo, males were treated with water-soluble hair spray. Most of the birds removed this dye within 24 hours by preening and washing. Therefore, the effects of the treatment were studied for one hour shortly after dyeing. Each experimental male was given three different treatments at intervals of at least two days: dyed black, dyed white, and, as a control, handled without dyeing. The seven resident males, who had been housed in the same group, engaged in aggressive encounters more often after dyeing than after the control treatment. The number of conflicts did not differ when individuals were dyed white or black. This aggressiveness might arise from the behaviour of other males, reacting to the dyed males as strangers, or from a change in feedback of the individual's own plumage colour. In any case these findings do not suggest that aggression is influenced by relative darkness. However, Amelia Segre also found that a male was more often displaced if he was dyed white than black, and, further, that the proportion of conflicts initiated by a dyed male was higher if he was black than if he was white. This indicates that behaviour does alter after a change in relative darkness. This may be a direct effect, but may also be caused by the reactions of other males. The effects of dyeing were most pronounced during the first few minutes after release. The decrease of aggression, somewhat later, seems to be due to individual recognition, an interpretation supported by a prolonged and very aggressive reaction to a strange resident male, dyed white.

Amelia Segre also studied the effects of artificially colouring a satellite male. Her data refer to only one individual, dyed in two successive seasons. Direct effects on the behaviour of this individual could not be demonstrated, but indirect effects, through the behaviour of other resident males, seemed to be related to the new colour. When this satellite male was dyed white, resident males tended to attack him less often than when he was dyed black. This might indicate that light males with satellite behaviour suffer less aggression from resident males than dark males with satellite behaviour. Since the satellite's own plumage was white too, this result may also indicate a tendency of resident males to behave aggressively towards strange satellites.

> My own dyeing experiments, conducted in the field, were less successful. Instead of water-soluble dyes, I used permanent hair dyes for two reasons. First, wild ruffs, especially satellites, cannot easily be caught. By using a permanent dye, I could maximize the data available from each individual. Second, ruffs may disappear for a few days after catching during which time water-soluble dyes would have been washed off. However, to apply these dyes, I had to keep the birds for 30 minutes. The most serious consequence was that the two resident males given a light plumage were not seen back on their residences. I dyed two satellites black and one of them also disappeared. The other satellite was seen again one day later. Apart from its plumage colour, which actually turned out to be grey, I did not observe any peculiar after-effects in this individual. He behaved like a normal satellite and was treated like a normal satellite by the other males.

The results of the dyeing experiments do not exclude the possibility that under particular circumstances the behaviour of a male is directly influenced by his own plumage. Besides, the experiments suggest that the behaviour of a male is moulded by the other males' reactions to his plumage, an idea also supported by some of my data from Roderwolde. For example, the dark resident males with independent plumage types suffer less aggression than the lighter-coloured resident males with atypical plumage types. I want to emphasize that this trend differs from a 'commonsense' expectation that the males with the lightest plumage suffer least aggression: under normal conditions the light-coloured satellite males on a lek are rarely attacked, but the dark-coloured independent males may be frequently attacked. Also, the result of Amelia Segre's dyeing experiment with a satellite is at variance with this trend. However, the comparison between light and dark independent males refers to categories with the same type of behaviour, whereas the comparison between satellites and independent males refers to categories which differ both in plumage and in behaviour. Tolerance by resident males towards satellites seems to depend on a combination of plumage and behaviour, and may be further strengthened by individual recognition. The darkness of the plumage of satellites does not seem to be very important in resident satellite interactions. The darkness of the plumage of independent males does seem to be important in interactions between resident males.

> The observed trend that light-coloured independent males suffer more aggression than dark-coloured ones might be a consequence of another trend which also became apparent from the Roderwolde data. The level of aggression, measured by the frequency of attacks upon other males, is higher in dark-coloured independent males than in light-coloured ones. This is in line with the outcome of Amelia Segre's dyeing experiments with resident males in which the frequency of being displaced and the proportion of initiatives for aggression appeared to be influenced by the darkness of the plumage. The high tendency for dark males to attack might inhibit other males from attacking them because any attack on a dark male would certainly be reciprocated.

Atypical plumage

The hypothesis regarding genetic control offers an explanation for status in males with independent and satellite plumage types. For the status of males with atypical plumage types, however, I cannot give a reasonable explanation based on genes. Some of the males with atypical plumage types obtain independent status, others satellite status, but there is no clear relationship with particular characteristics of their own plumage. However, the status of an individual with an atypical plumage type does seem to be related to the plumage types of the other males present on a lek: leks are mainly inhabited by independent males with atypical plumage types when the majority of the satellites possess a satellite plumage type. Conversely, leks are mainly inhabited by independent males with independent plumage types when the majority of the satellites possess an atypical plumage type. Bear in mind that independent plumage types are darker than atypical plumage types, and further that atypical plumage types are darker than satellite plumage types. Thus, on some leks, both independent males and satellites are relatively dark, and on other leks both independent males and satellites are relatively light, but combinations of relatively dark independent males with relatively light satellites, or of relatively light independent males with relatively dark satellites, are uncommon. It seems as if a fairly constant difference is maintained on leks between the plumage types of satellites and independent males. Similarly, the relative darkness of the satellites and the darkness of the independent males on the same lek or in the same area change in parallel in successive seasons. For example, Figure 25 depicts the changes in plumage types among resident males and satellites visiting the leks in Roderwolde from 1968 to 1972. During this period the proportion of dark males, both independent and satellite, gradually increased.

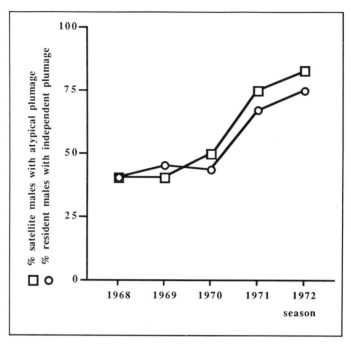

FIGURE 25 *The changes in the frequencies of plumage types in satellite (squares) and resident males (circles) from 1968 to 1972 in Roderwolde.*

The gradual change in the frequencies of plumage types in Roderwolde was associated with a sudden change in the distribution of copulations among males with different plumage types. During the first three years, when independent plumage types were relatively rare among resident males, such a male got on average only about one third of the copulations performed by a resident male with an atypical plumage type. However, during the next two years, when independent plumage types were relatively common among resident males, such a male got on average two to three times as many copulations as performed by a resident male with an atypical plumage type (Figure 26). Thus, dark males on a dark lek (independent plumage types predominating among independent males and atypical plumage types predominating among satellites) and light males on a light lek (atypical plumage types predominating among independent males and satellite plumage types among satellites), are more successful than dark males on a light lek and light males on a dark lek. In other words, the success of a male seems to be determined by the frequency of his own plumage type on the lek on which he stays.

I also tried to find out whether frequency of plumage types was related to a tendency to stay on the lek. The data collected in 1968 and 1971 on the leks A and B in Roderwolde were used for this analysis. In 1968 light males were common, in 1971 dark males. In both seasons males with plumage belonging to

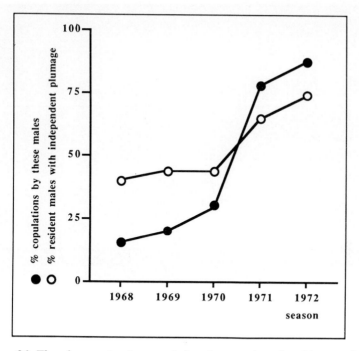

FIGURE 26 *The changes in the copulation frequencies of resident males with different plumage types (black dots) compared with changes in the frequencies of these plumage types (open dots) from 1968 to 1972 in Roderwolde.*

the common type tended to spend more time on the lek than males with plumage belonging to the rare type. The majority of the resident males with a rare plumage type defended a residence on the lek for less than five days, whereas the majority of the resident males with a common plumage type occupied a residence on the lek for at least five days. Similarly, satellite males with plumage belonging to the rare type tended to spend a shorter proportion of their time on the lek than satellite males with plumage belonging to the common type. This implies that males with plumage of the rare type on a given lek tend to migrate to other leks. It is probable that this tendency to migrate follows from a bird's particular experience on the lek. If it were a direct consequence of the behaviour of the other males, one should expect the males with the common plumage types to attack more often, but be less often attacked than the males with the rare plumage types. I could not find such a relationship. Therefore the tendency to migrate, displayed by males with plumage belonging to the rare type, seems to be due to the preference of females for males with a common plumage type.

Although my data collected on the leks near Roderwolde strongly support the idea that females prefer to copulate with males possessing common plumage types, I must admit that this hypothesis is compromised by other data. The results collected by Julia Shepard on Öland concerning female solicitations for copulation do not agree with this

Lek B near Roderwolde, 1967. Yellow-face in the middle background, Orange-face in front of him, squatting with a brown satellite.

idea. On all three leks which she studied, females tended to solicit males belonging to the rare plumage group rather than those belonging to the common plumage group.

The hypothesis predicts that some kind of experience on the lek by males with atypical plumage types depends on the proportion of dark males on that lek. On leks with a high proportion of dark males, males with atypical plumage types would tend to favour a satellite role. On leks with a low proportion of dark males, males with atypical plumage types would favour an independent role. Young males in our captive groups at the laboratory established their roles during the first lekking season when they were approximately one year old, or in the season following. Thus, it is certainly not impossible that the first experience on a lek is important for the development of roles, especially in males with atypical plumage types. In view of the observed differences in success, one would predict that the probability of such a male adopting a fixed independent role is reduced by early experience on a lek with a high proportion of dark males, and increased on a lek with a high proportion of light males.

Two students, Yolanda Holthuijzen and Bert van Dijk, tried to test these predictions on the birds held in aviaries. In the first experiment six young males were housed together with four adult resident males and six females. Two of the adult males had independent plumage types, and two had atypical plumage types. The plumage types of the young males were not apparent when the experiment started, but after some time two of them developed an independent plumage type, and four an atypical plumage type. It is evident that the males with independent plumage types would develop into independent males. However, it is difficult to predict status development in the birds with atypical plumage types. Because of the presence of two independent and two atypical plumage types among the adult males, the 'lek' can be neither considered as 'dark' nor 'light'. Because of the absence of adult satellite males, one might expect that males with atypical plumage types would develop into satellites. Because four of the young males had atypical plumage types, however, it is unlikely that all these males would develop into satellites. If that were the case, the proportion of satellites in the experimental population (40%) would become much higher than under natural conditions. Thus, some of these young males with atypical plumage types were expected to develop into satellites. This was in fact the case. Towards the end of the first season, the two males with independent plumage types and one of the males with an atypical plumage type established a residence. One other male with an atypical plumage type established a residence during his second season. The two remaining males with atypical plumage types started to behave like satellites in their second season. Although the outcome of the experiment is compatible with the expectation, other explanations may fit equally well.

In the second experiment five young males were brought together with females and adult satellites with satellite plumage types. After some time three of the young males developed independent plumage types and the other two aquired atypical plumage types. Under such conditions my hypothesis predicts that males with atypical plumage types will develop independent status. Until the end of April of the first season, aggressive behaviour was mainly shown by the adult satellite males. Thereafter most aggression occurred between the young males. Initially most activity was performed by the males with independent plumage types, but after some time the relation between plumage type and activity disappeared. One of the males with an independent plumage type established a residence. All the other young males sometimes joined this territory owner, especially when he was not visited by females. During those sessions both the young males with atypical plumage types and those with independent plumage types displayed behaviour characteristic of satellites. Yet in none of these males did fixation of the satellite role occur. This became obvious in the second year, when the adult satellites were removed and replaced by a group of adult independent males. All five youngsters established a residence, and thus assumed the role of an independent male. In that season a new yearling male with an atypical plumage type was added to the group. Where males only have the independent status my hypothesis predicts that this male would develop into a satellite. That prediction was not met. In spite of continuous attacks by the other males, even this yearling succeeded in establishing a residence. This unexpected development, however, could be the consequence of the behaviour of one of the adult males. Notwithstanding an earlier classification as an independent male, this bird clearly showed the behaviour of a satellite.

It is a pity that this kind of experiment requires an enormous investment of time, that the plumage of a ruff cannot be described before the age of one year, and that status development may take even longer. Because of these difficulties in the planning of such experiments, the results are mostly not very convincing. One may conclude that the possibility of environmental control of status in males with atypical plumage types has not been rejected, but that the evidence for it is still rather poor.

Physiological control

The relation between status and plumage might also arise from physiological factors, such as the male sex hormone testosterone. During the 1930s, Van Oordt and Junge had already demonstrated that castrated ruffs fail to develop nuptial plumage, including the wattles at the base of the bill, indicating that plumage development is under the control of testosterone. Moreover, there is a close association between moult phase and testis development. Detlev Drenck-hahn found that testis volume in males with non-breeding and prenuptial plumage was around $23 \, mm^3$ (per testis), whereas in males moulting from prenuptial to nuptial plumage (see Section 4.2) testis volume varied between 28 and $306 \, mm^3$. In males in full nuptial plumage, testis volume was around $1200 \, mm^3$.

Testosterone might also play a role in the dark pigmentation of independent males. In several analogous cases an obvious relationship was found between the intensity of black pigmentation and an individual's status in the dominance hierarchy. For instance, in winter flocks of the Harris' Sparrow, Sievert Rohwer found that birds with large areas of black feathers on their throats and crowns were dominant over birds with small black areas. Järvi and Bakken demonstrated that the width of the black breast-stripe in the Great Tit was also related to dominance. Similarly, Slagsvold and Lifjeld have shown that male Pied Flycatchers with conspicuous black-and-white plumage possess better territories than males with brownish plumage. Many studies confirm that social status is closely related to the level of testosterone circulating in the blood, and in some cases it has proved possible to demonstrate a direct effect of testosterone on social status. Rohwer and Rohwer were able to increase the social status of a Harris' Sparrow by a combination of two treatments: dyeing more feathers black, and administering testosterone. Silverin increased social status in Pied Flycatcher males by administering testosterone alone. It has been found by Røskraft *et al.* that dark Great Tits and Pied Flycatchers had a higher metabolic rate than their lighter-coloured conspecifics. Such differences in metabolic rates may also be a consequence of differing levels of testosterone. Similarly, the amount of dark pigment in the feathers may be under the control of testosterone levels at the time of plumage moult.

In the Ruff, marginal males, especially young birds, usually possess smaller nuptial feathers, fewer wattles and less brilliant colours than the resident males and the satellites who regularly visit the lek. Such differences in morphology and status might be due to different hormone levels. It is conceivable also that the difference between independent males (with dark plumage and high aggression) and satellites (with light plumage and almost no aggression) is associated with distinct hormone levels. It is quite suggestive that the so-called naked-nape males, who still possess their prenuptial plumage, and thus have small testes and low testosterone levels, may alternate between independent and satellite behaviour. However, experimental data regarding the effects of testosterone administration are almost completely lacking. Only two pilot experiments were conducted by Amelia Segre in the ruffs in the New York Zoo. Both suggest that testosterone influences aggressive behaviour, but that the action of the hormone might differ between independent males and satellites.

One marginal male given a 20-mg pellet of testosterone was reintroduced to the group one week later. Before this treatment the male seemed to avoid any aggressive encounter and never took the initiative in a conflict. Immediately after reintroduction the male initiated encounters by performing the forward display and by displacing other males. He also became involved in a number of fights. After 30 minutes, however, his aggressive behaviour ceased. From then onwards he resumed his avoidance of the other males, a change in behaviour which could not be explained. Possibly, the decrease in his aggression was due to a fight in which he was defeated by another male. That testosterone implantation in a marginal male does not lead to a permanent change in status agrees with observations by Rohwer. In Harris' Sparrows status could only be raised if both plumage colouration and testosterone level were changed. In the case of the Ruff, it is conceivable that the marginal male's small nuptial feathers provided the resident males with a cue to his low status, leading to a continuation of the aggression by resident males.

A second male, who received a similar dose of testosterone, was a white satellite. He started to vigorously court females after reintroduction, but initially failed to show aggressive behaviour towards males. After about one week, however, the satellite started to perform forward displays and charges, and also became involved in fights. Thus, after prolonged action of the hormone, aggressive behaviour was also affected. The satellite clearly took more initiatives after treatment than before. Additionally, he started to behave more like satellite males in the field. He visited the resident males on their territories and also performed the squat when he joined a resident male. Thus, administration of testosterone had a strong influence on the behaviour of this satellite. Superficially these data may suggest that testosterone levels are low in satellites. However, since nothing is known about the effect of the same treatment in a resident male, it cannot be excluded that such treatment leads to a similar increase of courtship and aggression. Thus, it remains possible that testosterone levels are the same in satellites and independent males. However, in view of the different effects in the two males tested above, one might propose that the action of the hormone differs between independent males and satellites.

Summary

In several species of animals, dominance is only one of the possible ways of achieving reproductive success. Submissive males may reproduce (1) by utilizing periods when dominants lose control over the females, (2) by intercepting females attracted by dominants, (3) by deception of dominants by mimicking females, or (4) in exchange for help. In the Ruff, satellite males make use of all four possibilities. Yet satellite males do not seem to be just making the best of a bad job. Calculations on mating frequencies suggest that, on average, a satellite male has the same reproductive success as an independent male. This is an important condition if status is controlled by genes. Genetic control of status is supported by the constancy of satellite and independent roles throughout adult life, constancy of plumage, and relationship between status and plumage. It may be argued that status and some aspects of the plumage are controlled by only one gene with two alternative alleles, males with atypical plumage types being heterozygotes. Experiments in which the plumage colours of adult males were artificially changed also suggest a direct influence of plumage colour on behaviour. The status of adult ruffs with atypical plumage types seems to be associated with the plumage colours of other males on the same lek. Most of them are satellites when independent plumage types are common, but independent when satellite plumage types are common. Mating success seems to increase with increasing frequency of the same plumage type. In young ruffs with atypical plumage types, the plumage colours of other ruffs in their direct environment seem to be important for status development. When most other ruffs are dark, these young males seem to develop into satellites, but when most other ruffs are light, they seem to develop into independent males. The male sex hormone testosterone is discussed as a proximate factor in establishing status differences between resident and marginal males, in determining plumage darkness, and in creating the behavioural differentiation between satellites and independent males. The action of the hormone, however, might be different in the latter two classes of male.

CHAPTER 3

The vigilant mother

During late spring and early summer it becomes difficult to detect Ruffs in their breeding habitat. The males no longer visit the leks, and most have left the area. Some of the females may still be sitting on their eggs, invisible to casual passers-by. When such disturbances remain at a distance they usually stay on their nests. On closer approach of the intruder, however, they may flush and run a dozen metres or so in a crouched posture through the vegetation before flying away without attracting attention. Towards the end of the incubation period, or during a sudden disturbance, a female may fly directly from her nest when danger is nearby. Such a conspicuous departure is usually followed by distraction displays in which the female moves around the source of the disturbance in an undulating, swerving flight-path. Now and then, usually when she comes close to the intruder, she utters a sequence of short, soft nasal, 'ah-ah-ah' sounds. This swerving flight may be interrupted briefly by a landing, followed by a rodent-like run in front of the intruder, sometimes seemingly crippled or broken-winged. In this way females may lead humans or predators away from their nests or chicks. Aerial predators, such as crows, are mainly approached in normal flight. Small ground predators usually elicit the rodent-run. Large intruders, such as humans, may provoke both aerial and terrestrial distraction displays. After hatching, distraction displays become much more common, and only when humans or potential predators stay at a great distance do females guarding chicks remain hidden in the vegetation. As soon as such dangers draw closer, the reeve suddenly appears, performs the appropriate distraction display, and thus betrays the presence of her chicks or eggs.

In the Ruff all reproductive and parental activity after copulation is thus performed by the female. She makes a nest, incubates the eggs, guides the chicks towards places where they can find their food, broods them when they are cold, and ensures their safety by leading them to cover and by distracting potential predators.

3.1 BREEDING HABITAT

Despite the large number of females seen in Roderwolde, either foraging or at leks, I never encountered a nest or observed many females who showed signs of having eggs or young, suggesting that the meadows around the Roderwolde leks were not very suitable for nesting.

The Lauwersmeer area

In 1977 and the two years thereafter I gained somewhat more experience of nesting reeves in the Lauwersmeer area, but it was by a stroke of luck. In that year Gerard Baerends, Jan Veen and I started a field study on communication in Black-headed Gulls. The research was done in a large breeding colony in a reclaimed area, the Lauwersmeer, covering about 9000 ha, and enclosed in 1969. Before reclamation the area was an estuary connected with the Wadden-sea, with salt marshes, and vast sandbanks separated by channels and gullies in the tidal zone. In the early spring we saw very large groups of Ruffs in the area. In the first years only a few of these birds tended to visit fixed locations, comparable to leks. In later years the tendency to lek became more and more pronounced, and in the late spring and early summer we found quite a number of reeves with nests. Some of these could easily be detected on the former sandbanks, which were sparsely overgrown. Many other nests remained hidden in the taller vegetation. Most reeves were breeding in the neighbourhood of Redshanks, Black-tailed Godwits, Lapwings, Oystercatchers, and even Avocets, and were quite often not far from the breeding colonies of Black-headed Gulls.

After reclamation, the area was colonized by many species of breeding birds whose population changes have been monitored by detailed censuses. Menno-bart Van Eerden and his co-workers found that from 1969 to 1975 the population of breeding reeves remained at approximately 20 nests over the whole area, but from 1975 to 1976 the population suddenly increased from 50 to about 150. Wibe Altenburg and co-workers found a further increase during the late 1970s and early 1980s up to about 400 nests, i.e. about 10 nests per km^2 of suitable habitat. This represents a considerable part of the Dutch breeding population, which, on the basis of data collected around 1980, was estimated by Van Dijk at 1250–1500 breeding females.

The soil of the former banks in the Lauwersmeer is sandy with many empty shells, and still somewhat brackish. The surrounding waters are fresh and the level is held constant at about 1 m below mean sea level. In contrast to the salt marshes outside the sea-dykes, the area never becomes inundated by saline water. However, during periods of heavy rain and northern storms, especially in winter and early spring, the lower parts may become flooded with fresh water because the low tides are too brief to flush the excess water to the Waddensea. Under these conditions the vegetation remains fairly sparse and seems to be suitable for nesting. Moreover, the availability of food for chicks appears to be rich under these circumstances.

Other breeding areas in the temperate zone

In fact, many of the known breeding areas of the Ruff have much in common with the Lauwersmeer area. The polder Het Noorden on the island of Texel, where Edmond Selous did his classical field study, was a former salt marsh, enclosed at the beginning of the nineteenth century. Parts of this polder remained somewhat brackish until the sea-dykes were raised about ten years ago. Up to the middle of this century parts of the polder became submerged during winter. The polder Waal en Burg on the same island, which was recommended by Jacob Thijsse for observing Ruffs, was enclosed much earlier, but parts of it still remained brackish until quite recently and were flooded in winter. The population of breeding reeves in the northwestern part of the Netherlands, north of Amsterdam, remained fairly large until about 1960. The most important breeding areas for this population were also polders which were wet during the winter, and were still somewhat brackish until quite recently. The peninsula Tipperne in Denmark, where F. Søgaard Andersen, Peter Bancke and Horst Meesenburg studied Ruffs, is situated in an inland sea, Rinkøbing fjord, which was connected with the North Sea up to 1935. Colonization by Ruffs occurred shortly after enclosure, when the salt in the area gradually disappeared. In this area also, water levels could rise in winter and inundate the lower parts of the peninsula. Although the area is now managed as a sanctuary, the number of breeding reeves has declined, apparently mainly as a result of the strong growth of the vegetation after desalination. A similar decline may also be expected in the near future for the Dutch population in the Lauwersmeer.

In the Baltic area also, reeves prefer saline and wet sites for breeding. Scheufler and Stiefel emphasized the importance of salt marshes for breeding on the East German island of Kirr. The soil of these salt marshes is peaty and the surface of the overgrown parts only 0.3–0.5 m above mean sea level. Tidal movements are weak in this area and the salt marshes are only occasionally flooded by heavy storms. The maximum height of the vegetation varies from 0.1 m in the grazed parts up to 0.4 m, reeves selecting the higher vegetation for nesting. On the Swedish island of Öland reeves mainly breed in the low and wet areas at the southeastern side of the island, close to the sea. Reeves in the Finnish population near Virkkula, studied by David Lank and Connie Smith, nested along the coast of the northeastern part of the Gulf of Bothnia in somewhat brackish grasslands, which may flood in early spring.

The presence of salt is certainly not required for reeves and their chicks to survive in a particular area but, in combination with other factors such as prolonged flooding during the winter, a saline substrate may be beneficial because the vegetation remains short. Short vegetation may also arise from other factors, such as a shortage of nutrients in the soil, and very low winter temperatures. Around the beginning of this century many breeding reeves were found in the northeastern part of the Netherlands, especially in Friesland, mainly in the low hay-fields which were not fertilized, and mown only once or twice a year. In winter these fields often became flooded. This breeding population was strongly affected by the increased use of fertilizers and lowered groundwater levels, enabling farmers to mow much earlier in the season. The initial reaction was a shift in the timing of breeding. Albert Beintema and his associates demonstrated that all Dutch meadow birds, the Ruff included, started breeding about two weeks earlier than at the beginning of this century. They also showed the strong decline of the Ruff population in the Netherlands during the last few decades to be due to modern agricultural practices. Frequent mowing, and trampling because of high grazing intensities, have led to almost complete nest failure of this species in Dutch meadow areas.

In the first half of this century, many of the reeves breeding in the Netherlands were also found in the water-meadows of the rivers Rhine, IJssel, Waal, Maas, Lek and Merwede. As in the Frisian breeding habitats, these areas were used as hay-meadows, and occasionally for grazing, while the water meadows were susceptible to river flooding, especially during winter and early spring. The decline of Ruffs in these areas can likewise be associated with the intensification of agriculture. At the start of this century reeves also nested in high numbers in central Europe, especially in the extensive moors bordering the Pripet River in southern Belorussia. The suitability of this area for Ruffs was the result of periodic flooding and simple agricultural methods, and the recent decline in numbers seems to be due to land drainage.

Northern habitats

In Fenno-Scandia and the northern part of the Soviet Union, reeves select large moors in the pine-forest areas for nesting, while further north or higher in the mountains they use the tundras above the treeline. In these areas vegetation remains short from the combined effects of severe frost in winter and flooding in early spring. I gained a general impression of such areas during a long trip through Lapland in the early summer of 1979. Finding Ruffs was a major reason for the trip, but unfortunately I was too late in the season to see any males. Reeves, however, were discovered in various places, apparently with nests or young.

All the females were close to puddles, pools, or small lakes. Many of these areas were characterized by the presence of cotton-grass, occasionally in small tussocks, but most often in broad strips bordering water. Quite often the relatively dry parts consisted of raised hummocks overgrown with dwarf willow, dwarf birch, heather, sedges, reindeer moss, and other mosses. The air was full of voracious mosquitos and other biting insects. Some of the reeves inhabited swampy areas in the taiga zone, from only a few hectares in extent up to several square kilometres. The sites chosen typically lacked trees, but were surrounded by open, or occasionally fairly closed, pine-forest or birch-woods. Some other reeves inhabited completely treeless, real tundra areas, which could also contain fairly dry and stony parts. In the same habitats I saw Greenshanks, Redshanks, Spotted Redshanks, Wood Sandpipers, Whimbrels, Bar-tailed Godwits, Red-necked Phalaropes, Golden Plovers, Arctic Terns, Willow Grouse, and Lapland Buntings. Outwardly the tundra breeding habitats, in particular, closely resembled the parts of the Lauwersmeer area I knew to be used by reeves, or the salt marshes I had read about on the Baltic island of Kirr, studied by Scheufler and Stiefel. I also suspect that the situation on the Tipperne peninsula was fairly similar to that on these more northerly breeding habitats, shortly after the enclosure of Ringkøbing fjord.

Summary

Reeves breed in temperate, boreal, subarctic and arctic areas. They prefer moist lowlands with short vegetation in spring and early summer: salt marshes, hay-meadows, water-meadows of rivers, and tundra, which may be saline, flooded during the winter and early spring, or have a limited availability of nutrients in the soil. For nesting they prefer sites with somewhat taller vegetation, quite frequently close to other waders. The decline of the Ruff population in western and central Europe is probably caused by land drainage and increased use of fertilizers.

3.2 PARENTAL CARE

Several of the nests I discovered in the Lauwersmeer area were in very short vegetation. They were so easily spotted, sometimes even from a moving car, that I cannot believe they represent the typical nesting site. Yet such an exposed position seems to be normal for reeves nesting on tundra. I also found, mostly by accident, a number of nests which were perfectly concealed in taller vegetation. Quite frequently I searched in vain for a nest after I had seen a reeve repeatedly flushed from approximately the same site. Usually, the nest resembled a small tunnel, roofed with grass in a tussock or in a zone of taller vegetation. The nest-cup, about 12 cm in diameter, was made in a small hollow, about 3 cm deep, lined with a 2-cm layer of grass-blades and other plant material. All the warm clutches which I discovered contained four eggs and were found in May or June.

There are no indications that females maintain nesting territories so as to space out over the available habitat. Observations by Khlebosolov in north-eastern Yakutia suggest that males maintain territories on the tundra, supplementary to their positions on leks, and that females nest in these territories and maintain short-lasting monogamous pair-bonds with the territory owner. These bonds would loosen after egg-laying, enabling some males to establish successive bonds with two females, both nesting in the same territory. This interpretation is highly interesting, but probably not applicable to the Ruffs of the southern breeding grounds: I cannot imagine the successful resident males of the Dutch leks maintaining territories in the nesting habitat, because they simply do not have the time to defend them.

The production of a four-egg clutch requires a considerable investment by the female. In May her average body weight is about 120 g, and a single egg weighs about 20 g. Eggs are laid at intervals ranging from 1 to 1.5 days, though the space between the third and fourth egg may be up to four days. Reeves spend less than an hour each day on the nest up to the third egg, after which they may sit on their nests for hours. Almost continuous incubation does not start before the last egg is laid.

There are some indications that under particular circumstances the relationship between males and females may be maintained during nesting. Heinz Mildenberger found that the females in a small population in OstFriesland, West Germany, nested close to the site frequented by their their mating partner. Three of the males in this population displayed mostly alone, each on a fixed site, while two of them displayed on a communal site. The males appeared to be able to detect distant predators and to warn the females nesting close to them, and even to attack and distract the predators. Detlev Drenckhahn summarized a number of similar cases.

There is no indication, however, that males share in the care of eggs and young. After laying the last egg, the reeve incubates for approximately three weeks. She is neither relieved nor fed by a partner, but has to care for herself and her offspring. Since females are unable to incubate and to forage at the same time, they are forced to leave their nests to avoid starvation. They cannot stay away for too long at a time because the eggs would cool down too much, especially in cold habitats. Usually, therefore, reeves interrupt incubation several times a day for short foraging trips.

The timing of incubation spells and foraging breaks of reeves and many other species of waders has been analysed by the Soviet ornithologist Kondratiev in northeastern Siberia. During the first week of incubation, reeves had 10–15 foraging breaks each day, each lasting about 15 minutes on cold days, and up to 30 minutes when it was warmer. On average, they spent about 83% of their time on the nest. During the second week, they took only six to eight foraging breaks per day, lasting 10–85 minutes, and spent about 90% of their time on the nest. During the last week of incubation, breaks lasted 2–50 minutes, with approximately 88% of the time spent incubating. Thus, in spite of the fact that reeves do not receive direct assistance from males in incubation, their nests remain warmed for a considerable proportion of the day. Species in which only one parent cares for the nest, such as Grey Phalaropes, Red-necked Phalaropes, Temminck's Stints, and Pectoral Sandpipers, spend about the same proportion of their time incubating as do reeves. Yet they do not achieve the same attentiveness as species with biparental care such as Grey Plovers, Turnstones, and Dunlins, whose clutches are incubated for 95–100% of the time. Kondratiev also measured the consequences of this for the temperature of the reeve's eggs. Temperature fluctuations were maintained within a range of 2°C. On cold days the inner egg temperature was kept at about 29°C and on warmer days at about 30.5°C. I found a similar value (nest temperature of 28°C) in the nest of a reeve belonging to the experimental group of Ruffs held in the laboratory.

This is a rather low value in comparison with most other birds, which usually maintain temperatures of 32–38°C. The temperature of the brood-patch, about 41°C, is quite normal and is therefore not responsible for the low temperature inside the egg. This temperature is probably the best compromise for maintaining a fairly constant value by only one parent under severe conditions. Moreover, it is possible that higher temperatures are harmful to the developing eggs. This might be deduced from our poor success at rearing eggs in an incubator adjusted for chicken eggs. Hatching success of these eggs was very low in comparison to eggs which were incubated by a female in the aviary. Moreover, the survival of young hatched in an incubator was also low. Initially, we thought that our incubator was too dry, but our success did not increase after raising the humidity. When, after I measured nest temperature, the incubation temperature was lowered, matters improved.

Three to five days before hatching, the chick pecks a little hole in the eggshell and keeps its bill poked through that hole. A few hours after hatching it may leave the nest and immediately start to peck at small moving objects, soon succeeding in catching small spiders and insects. The chicks only rarely interact with their siblings. During the first days after hatching they often return to the female to be brooded. Brooding during the night may continue up to the tenth day of life. During her stay with the young, the reeve is very attentive. She summons her young to hide when there is some danger and the soft nasal sounds uttered during her display when distracting a predator probably warn the young to remain hidden. On several occasions, both in the Dutch breeding habitats and in Lapland, I got the impression that different families stay very close together. Quite frequently several reeves seem to cooperate in a distraction display by joining another reeve who is already flying around an intruder. Different females possibly also cooperate in tending young. The reeve usually stays with her offspring until about two weeks after hatching, and then leaves them.

Summary

The nest is like a small tunnel in a tussock or an open cup in more exposed nesting habitats. Almost all clutches contain four eggs. Prolonged sitting on the nest begins after the third egg, but continuous warming does not start before the last egg is laid. Occasionally males share in nest defence against predators, but they never share in the care of eggs and young. Incubating reeves spend 80–90% of their time on the nest and take several short foraging breaks each day. The inner egg temperature is maintained at about 30°C. Chicks hatch after approximately three weeks of incubation, three to five days after pecking a hole in the eggshell. They may leave the nest after a few hours and start to forage on the same day. The female stays with her offspring for about two weeks after hatching, during which time she may brood the small chicks, and defend them throughout against predators, quite often in cooperation with other reeves.

3.3 DEVELOPMENT OF THE CHICKS

When a young Ruff emerges from the egg, its body weight is about 10% of the adult weight. To reach adult size all parts of the body must grow, but not to the same extent. The wings, for example, are still completely underdeveloped and have to grow considerably. At hatching, the bill has already reached 50% of its final size, the tarsi 60%, and the middle toes more than 90%! Thus, young Ruffs clearly possess the tools to walk and to eat. Flight develops much later, around 20 days of age.

The breeding experiments in our laboratory enabled me to watch the developing behaviour of the young chicks. To facilitate observation I took care of three young males in June 1969, all from the same clutch, incubated by their mother in the aviary, and kept in an incubator on the day of hatching. During the first days of life they were held in a wooden case, measuring 60 × 60 ×60 cm, with a lamp for warmth. The bottom was covered with moist turf, and the upper

side was partially open, and thus offered an unobstructed view of the chicks inside. In this hutch I had placed a shallow dish of water for drinking and bathing. During the first few days the chicks were mainly fed on spiders and insects, caught with a net. Additionally, they got a mixture of boiled egg-yolk, chopped ox-heart, ant eggs, dried food for insect-eating birds, brewer's yeast and calcium. After a week they were moved to a larger cage with gauze walls. Their diet was gradually changed to a menu of mainly dry food pellets as used in trout farms, which was also given to the birds in the aviary.

From the first day onwards the chicks uttered soft vocalizations, especially when they were close together or close to the lamp. Louder vocalizations were heard when they got cold or were separated from their siblings. From the first day of life they walked, and pecked at, and ate, moving objects. They further appeared to be able to drink, to preen, and to crouch almost undetected in the vegetation. On the second day they also performed hopping movements, which did not seem to be elicited by other individuals, nor directed towards them. Clear social interactions were not seen until the fifth day of life. Then two individuals would take up a position facing each other, extending their legs and necks, vocalizing loudly, and making contact with their bill-tips. After a few seconds they separated again without real pecking or other signs of overt aggression. On the sixth day such bill-to-bill contacts were observed frequently. The posture adopted during such contacts could have an intimidating effect on an opponent and sometimes led to pecking towards the opponent and chasing.

Aggressive encounters have also been observed by other investigators who tried rearing young Ruffs. Otto and Magdalena Heinroth emphasized that young Ruffs are very pugnacious. They reared two chicks up to about one week old, and saw clear signs of aggression shortly after hatching. Otto Von Frisch observed aggressive encounters at nine days between the three young females he reared. Ivanova observed aggressive encounters between males at as young an age as only three days. The first aggressive encounters among my birds were seen on the sixth day of life. From that day onwards, these encounters might occur at a very high frequency, but there were also long periods during which no aggression was apparent, and its frequency could fluctuate in an unpredictable manner. For instance, on the seventh day I saw 23 encounters in 30 minutes. On the eighth day, however, at the same time of the day and under the same conditions, I saw only one encounter in an observation session of the same length. Peaks in aggression were seen during the whole period during which I took care of the young Ruffs, ending when the birds were released at the age of two months into the big aviary with the other Ruffs. Ritualized adult behaviour patterns, such as bill-thrusting and the forward display, were exhibited from 30 days onwards. Prolonged fights were not seen before six weeks of age. The first copulation attempt was seen when the males were only one month old.

During my observations on the young birds I never saw behaviour resembling the interactions between resident males and satellites. Such behaviour was not observed till the next spring, when the males were one year old. Then they would associate in small groups of two or three birds, in which one of the males played the role of residence owner and the other one or two the role of satellite. However, the adoption of a satellite role by a yearling male does not imply that satellite status will be maintained during adult life.

Summary

Young Ruffs are independent at two weeks and able to fly at three weeks. Mutual aggression may be displayed when they are a few days old, and occurs frequently after one week. Ritualized displays are exhibited after one month, but interactions resembling those between resident males and satellites have not been observed before the Ruffs are one year old.

CHAPTER 4

Indolence or diligence?

In comparison with many of their close relatives, male Ruffs do not devote much effort to the care of their offspring. The females invest highly in parental care, but the males spend most energy on mutual competition. For males, the contributions to their offspring are mainly, or completely, restricted to the production of sperm and the act of insemination, so the male's costs of reproduction seem to be quite low. However, the male also has to invest considerably to meet the conditions enabling him to reproduce. An independent male has to acquire and maintain a residence for copulation and has to stay for many hours each day on a lek. A satellite male has to suffer the resident male's aggression to get the opportunity to copulate and also has to travel between leks to utilize the best opportunities open to him. Thus, the total effort spent on reproduction by a male might be in the same range as the effort spent by a female. If, however, the males invested extra effort in parental care, the Ruff should, on average, be able to rear more offspring. This implies that, on average, male Ruffs do not reproduce very efficiently. Hypothetically, they could do better.

Although the Ruff's reproductive efforts could, in theory, be used more efficiently in an absolute sense, they seem to be appropriate to the limitations dictated by the system. As in reproduction, survival is also under control of the Ruff's own machinery: its options and its restrictions. The 'machine' offers opportunities for long-distance movements, but the use of the machine is restricted by the need for special fuelling and periodical renewal of particular

Table 19 The breeding population of the Ruff in Europe around 1985 expressed in numbers of nests (after Piersma).

North Sea region	
Western Belgium	0–2
The Netherlands	800–1100
Ost Friesland and Schleswig-Holstein, West Germany	500
Denmark	650
England and Ireland	1–10
Southwestern Europe	
Atlantic coast of France	5–13
Central Europe	
East Germany	60–80
Poland	350–400
Hungary	8–10
Northern Europe	
Norway	15 000
Sweden	80 000
Finland	150 000

components. In Sections 4.1–4.6 I want to discuss the functioning of the Ruff as such a machine against the background of its population dynamics. I further want to pay special attention to the efficiency of the organism within the constraints to which it is subject.

4.1 DISTRIBUTION

Ruffs have been found almost all over the world. Most Ruffs stay within the palearctic region (Europe and much of Asia and part of Africa), but several sightings have been reported from northern, central, and southern America, and even from Australia. A Ruff rarely stays longer than half a year at the same place. It tends to wander, but not at random, sticking to particular rules. An individual may visit the same place during successive years, using the various stations for different purposes: for breeding, wintering, moulting, and foraging. Therefore, the Ruff's distribution over the world cannot be considered apart from the roles that the different geographical areas play in its life.

Breeding

Data on numbers of breeding Ruffs in Europe, mainly from the early 1980s, have been derived from a review on breeding waders compiled by Theunis Piersma. They are summarized in Table 19. Here I assume that the number of

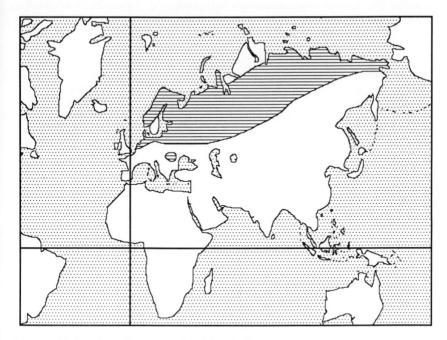

Figure 27 *The breeding grounds of the Ruff.*

breeding 'pairs', referred to in the review, is equivalent to the number of nests. Additional data have been taken from handbooks. A summary of breeding distribution is presented in Figure 27.

Nesting reeves and lekking ruffs have been found around the North Sea, where present numbers are fairly low, or very low, altogether about 2000 nests. In contrast, at the beginning of this century, this area was extensively populated by Ruffs, there probably being more than 10 000 nests. During the eighteenth and nineteenth centuries, nesting reeves were also common in England and Ireland. Here, their numbers decreased due to drainage of the breeding grounds and hunting. Ruffs were known as a highly expensive delicacy in Britain and disappeared in 1922, but re-established in very small numbers from 1963 onwards.

The populations of breeding reeves and lekking ruffs in central Europe are small, altogether roughly 500 nests. They have declined sharply during the second half of this century. In northern Europe, reeves breed in considerable numbers totalling hundreds of thousands of nests. In Russia, Ruffs seem to breed in fairly high numbers in the lowlands southeast of Moscow and also in the north. Very large populations of Ruffs seem to breed in the extensive tundra from western to eastern Siberia.

Table 20 The numbers of wintering Ruffs (after Glutz *et al.*, Cramp and Simmons, and Davidson and Pienkowski).

Western Africa (around 1965)	
Senegal: delta Senegal river	1 000 000
Guinea-Bissau: rice fields	50 000–75 000
Mali: inundation zone Niger River	>1 000 000
Nigeria: Sokote river	>1 000 000
Nigeria: delta River Yobe in Lake Chad	±1 000 000
Eastern and southern Africa	
South Africa: mainly coastal wetlands	22 000
Burundi: Rizizi marshes	±10 000
Uganda: shores Lake Edward and surrounding swamps	±10 000
Kenya: inland wetlands	19 000
Ethiopia: Rift Valley lakes	±10 000
Sudan: inland	300 000–1 000 000
Egypt	1 000–2 000
Asia	
Western India, Pakistan: Indus delta	>8 000
Eastern India, Bangladesh	±500
Iran	±500
Iraq	±2 000
Turkey	±1 000
Europe	
Italy, southern France and Spain: Mediterranean area	±3 000
Bulgaria: Black Sea coast	200–2 000
France: Atlantic coast	500–5 000
Great Britain and Ireland: southern coast	±1 500
Belgium and southwestern Netherlands	±2 000
Northern Netherlands	±800

Wintering

Data on distribution and numbers of wintering Ruffs have been derived from handbooks, and from a recent report on the conservation of flyway populations of waders, edited by Davidson and Pienkowski. A review of these data is presented in Table 20 and in Figure 28. Four main wintering areas can be distinguished:

(1)   Western Africa, south of the Sahara, perhaps with several millions of wintering individuals in the 1960s, but fewer now. For instance, the whole winter population in the Senegal delta was counted in 1987 by the OAG of Münster and assessed at only 80 000 individuals, less than one tenth of the estimate by Morel and Roux around 1970.

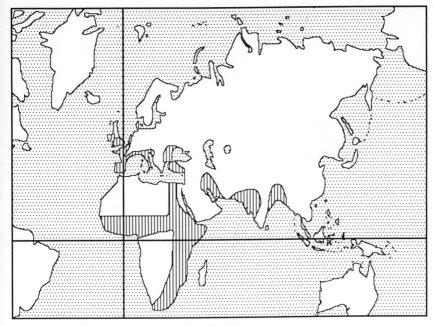

FIGURE 28 *The winter quarters of the Ruff.*

(2) Eastern and southern Africa, with hundreds of thousands of birds, especially in Sudan.
(3) Asia, especially northwestern India, with more than 10 000 birds.
(4) Europe, with another 10 000 birds.

Moulting and foraging

The distance between breeding grounds and winter quarters is rarely covered in one hop, Ruffs calling at various stations on the way. Most of these are visited for foraging to build up new reserves. Also, during the summer some Ruffs may visit particular stations for a longer period. These stopovers are used for moulting. They may be visited by large numbers of Ruffs who concentrate during the night on communal roosts, located in shallow puddles or on wet meadows. Individuals may stay for months in the same area. They may complete the whole process of wing-moult, or may interrupt moulting, and leave the area before wing-moult is concluded. Moulting areas also seem to be important for building up new fat reserves and are known from western Europe and from the Volga delta at the northwestern side of the Caspian Sea. The main moulting areas are shown in Figure 29.

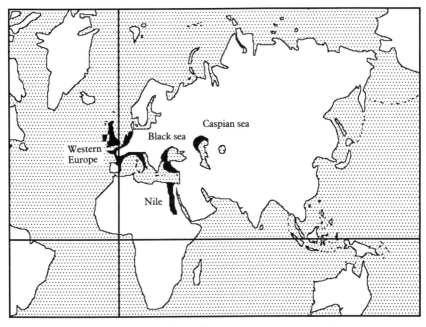

FIGURE 29 *The main resting and moulting areas during migration.*

The sewage farms near Münster, West Germany, studied by Michael Haren-gerd and by other members of the OAG (Ornithologische Arbeitsgemeinschaft or Ornithological Working-Community) of Münster, form one of the best known foraging and moulting areas for Ruffs in western Europe. Especially during the late 1960s and early 1970s, this area was visited by many Ruffs, both in early spring and in summer. In early spring, from the beginning of April to the end of May, the Ruffs stayed only for foraging. Males were present for about two weeks, and females for about one week, generally at relatively low numbers at any one time, with a peak of around 200 birds. In summer, from the end of June to the middle of October, visitors, especially males, stayed for moulting and foraging. Moulting males spent on average six weeks in the area, moulting females almost four weeks, and non-moulting adults about two weeks. The number of Ruffs present simultaneously could be fairly high during the summer, with peak numbers of the order of 800.

In summer, migrating Ruffs pass through the Netherlands in great numbers. From the beginning of July up to the beginning of October, 20 000–100 000 may be present in the country on the same day, with peak numbers occurring at the beginning of August. According to Klaas Koopman, many of these birds stay and moult there. About 60% of the males and females caught in the middle of July had started wing-moult. By the middle of August all the males and about 90% of the females had started to moult, but approximately 20% of both sexes showed interrupted wing-moult ('suspended moult'). Around the beginning of September the first males and females had completed wing-moult, and by the middle of October almost all birds in the Netherlands had completed their moult. Wing-moult occurs in various other areas in western Europe. Large numbers of Ruffs moult on the coasts of the North Sea in Schleswig-Holstein, West Germany, and in Britain moulting birds are also common. Many Ruffs, however, especially females, conclude wing-moult in their winter quarters.

Site-fidelity

Ruffs display a strong tendency to return to the places which they have used in the past, as can be deduced from recoveries of ringed birds. Gabriëlle Van Dinteren took up the challenge of analysing the complete Euring data files on the Ruff up to 1981, supplemented by the reports of various ringing stations and direct information from these stations, totalling 1912 recoveries. The analysis of this material might have been a tedious task, but she turned it into thrilling detective work. Out of 1384 individuals eligible for a study of site-fidelity, 43 (3%) were recovered within six months, and 39 (3%) up to eight years after ringing at the same geographical coordinates (to within minutes). Of these 82 birds, 54 were ringed and recovered within the breeding range, five were ringed and recovered in the winter quarters, and the remaining 23 were ringed and recovered in areas which may be traversed during migration, but which may also be used for wintering. Site-fidelity is even more pronounced in the recoveries of Ruffs ringed as nestlings. Out of 16 individuals, six (almost 40%) were recovered as adults one or more years after ringing (in May or June) at the same geographical coordinates (again to within minutes). The best evidence for site-fidelity, however, derives from detailed studies of breeding, wintering, and moulting areas.

F. Søgaard Andersen concluded as early as 1948 and 1951 that both male and female Ruffs tend to visit the same breeding ground year after year, and that, in addition, reeves seem to display a tendency to return to their birthplace. Lidy Hogan-Warburg's data on the males of Schiermonnikoog, and my own data on the males near Roderwolde (see Table 3), are fully in accordance with Andersen's results.

From 1944 to 1948 on Tipperne, Denmark, Andersen caught 40 different females on nests and 56 different males on leks. Seven females were caught in different seasons. Two of these were ringed as nestlings in the same area. On the basis of the numbers of birds ringed and recaptured and the total number of nests, Andersen calculated that 25–60% of females return the following year. All recaptured females built their nests within 150 m of the nest where they were ringed as an adult or nestling. Eleven males were caught in successive seasons. None of these were ringed as nestlings. In the five successive years, the percentage of birds returning varied between 15% and 100%.

A Ruff also tends to stay on a particular wintering site for a fairly long period, and to return to that area the next winter. This conclusion has been drawn by D.J. Pearson on the basis of recaptures of Ruffs in Kenya. Of 3533 birds ringed near Lake Nakuru, 213 were retrapped, mostly over periods of two months or more. From these retraps 130 birds were caught one or more seasons after the first capture. Based on the proportion of birds retrapped after one, two, three, four, and five seasons, Pearson calculated that each year about 40% of the population was replaced as a result of mortality and change of wintering area, and thus that approximately 60% of the birds returned to the same wintering site in the following year.

Ruffs also show a strong tendency to return to the same moulting area, though not to a seasonal foraging ground, as can be seen from the data collected by Michael Harengerd and the other members of the OAG of Münster. From re-sightings of colour-ringed birds in the moulting area, they calculated that each year about 30% of the population of moulting Ruffs disappears, probably due to mortality.

Birds visiting the area only to forage and build up fat reserves during the spring were rarely re-sighted in subsequent years or during the summer migration. Only five out of 552 Ruffs (1%) colour-ringed during the spring migration were seen the next spring. A slightly higher proportion of those colour-ringed in spring, 27 out of 757 (4%), returned the following summer. The proportion returning in spring after capture in summer was also low (25 out of 1479: 2%). However, the Ruffs which visited the area for wing-moult tended to return summer after summer. Almost 30% of all birds, colour-ringed as adults during summer, returned the next summer. Six years after ringing, 3% of these birds still visited the area to moult! To investigate site-fidelity in a more experimental way, 23 males and 54 females were transported to Göttingen, about 170 km east-southeast of Münster, and released. All but one of the males, compared with only 19 of the females, were moulting at the time of capture. The moulting birds in particular tended to return within a few days to the sewage-farms near Münster near where they were caught. Similarly, many of the moulting birds were re-sighted the next summer, but almost none of the non-moulting females. The birds colour-ringed as juveniles during the summer were less likely to return next summer: about 15% of the males and 7% of the females. The difference between adults and juveniles may be connected with the fact that juveniles stay for a shorter time because they do not moult their flight feathers during the first summer (see Section 4.3). Besides, juveniles may suffer higher mortality rates than adults and may stay in the winter quarters during their first spring and second summer. This might be deduced from the fact that, of the juveniles which did not return after one year, several did return for wing-moult after an absence of two, three, or even four years!

Nomadism

Usually the life of a Ruff seems to proceed at a limited number of fixed locations, which are visited year after year to a fixed timetable. Yet some Ruffs may wander away from their usual routes, as demonstrated by the observation that:

— Ruffs have been observed almost all over the world;
— Ruffs readily settle in suitable breeding habitats which become suddenly available;

— Ruffs ringed on particular breeding grounds may later be found breeding long distances away.

Ruffs may wander from the eastern coasts of Asia up to Alaska, where D.D. Gibson found a nest, and perhaps even to the shores of Hudson's Bay, where J.D. Reynolds observed a displaying male with three females. Further south, they reach Japan, the Mariana islands, the Philippines, New Guinea, and Australia, mainly from September to April. They may also stray from the eastern coasts of Africa, to the Seychelles, Mauritius, and Madagascar. From the western coasts of the Palearctic they may wander to Iceland, Greenland, and on to the eastern seaboard of North America. In addition, they may stray to Ireland, the Azores, and the Canary Islands. In the New World, Ruffs have been found all over the United States, in Venezuela, on Trinidad, and even in Peru.

The usual breeding habitat of the Ruff is unstable, because of the action of ice, snow, and water during the winter and early spring. This implies that the location of suitable breeding sites might change between years. Therefore, it may pay for a reeve to be flexible in her choice of a breeding site and to be ready to establish herself in a new area. I have already discussed the establishment of nesting reeves in suitable new habitats, such as the Lauwersmeer area in the Netherlands, and the Tipperne peninsula in Denmark (see Section 3.1). The very rapid increase of nests in the Lauwersmeer area may be of further interest. By the fifteenth year after the area was viable for settlement, about 400 nests were present. This increase seemed to proceed much faster than the establishment of males on fixed leks, even though considerable numbers of males wandered through the area.

Movement of birds between different breeding areas has also been demonstrated by Gabriëlle Van Dinteren from recovery data of ringed Ruffs. She showed that 14 Ruffs ringed in northwestern Europe (Finland, 4; Sweden, 4; Denmark, 2; Poland, 1; DDR, 1; Netherlands, 1; Britain, 1) had been recovered in the eastern part of the Soviet Union (east of 90°E). This is about 2% of the total recoveries used for analysing the relationship between the sites of ringing and recovery. Three of these birds, all males, were recovered in the same season. Considering that the probability of finding birds in this area of the Soviet Union is very low, one may conclude that large numbers of Ruffs wander between the western and eastern parts of the species' breeding range. The nomadic tendency is also seen in recoveries in the breeding season (in May or June) of birds ringed as nestlings. Of 16 recoveries, four were in other countries within the breeding range. Two birds born in Finland moved to the western part of the Soviet Union, while, of two others born in the Netherlands, one moved to Finland and the other to Poland.

Age distribution

Ruffs live in varying company. The composition of a population, as reflected by the proportions of birds of different classes, is related to the role of that population in the life of the Ruff. Breeding populations, wintering populations and moulting populations all differ in their demographic make-up. Moreover, the composition of a population is not constant, the proportions of different classes of birds varying with time. One key variable is the representation of the different age classes.

To my knowledge, data on the presence of second calendar-year Ruffs in the breeding areas are scarce, and not very accurate. From my numerous walks and trips around Roderwolde, I gained the impression that the older males were the first to return. They were evidently the ones who re-established the leks in early spring. At that time also, second-calendar-year males returned, but they tended to visit the leks as marginal males or peripheral satellites, although a few did establish themselves as resident males by the end of the season. I have no data regarding the proportion of such males in the population. It has been shown by F. Søgaard Andersen that second-calendar-year females are able to breed but I cannot make a reasonable guess about the proportion of such females in the Dutch breeding population. Their proportion in the breeding population of Kirr island, East Germany, has been estimated by Scheufler and Stiefel at 5–10%.

> This is much lower than the percentage of second-calendar-year birds observed on the sewage-farms near Münster during spring migration from the middle of March to the middle of May. The proportion of young birds among females was about 30% and remained quite constant during the whole period, while the proportion of young birds among males was even higher, on average 45%, and tended to rise towards the end of spring migration. This could imply that many second-calendar-year birds wander from one place to another without spending much time in the areas with leks and nests.

The age composition of wintering populations differs clearly between southern and northern winter quarters. In Africa the proportion of juveniles varies between 20% and 70%; in the southwestern part of the Netherlands, however, the proportion of juveniles is less than 10%. Thus, juveniles tend to wander further south than adults, and possibly also tend to spend summer in the southern wintering areas.

> Detailed data have been collected by D.J. Pearson in Kenya at lakes Nakuru and Magadi. He found small populations of second-calendar-year birds, especially females, who stayed in these areas during the summer from May to August. In early August the first birds, consisting only of adults, returned from the breeding grounds. Juveniles arrived from the end of August onwards. The proportion of juveniles among males seemed to be somewhat higher than among females. At Nakuru the proportion of juveniles increased from zero to about 40% in November, decreased again towards 20% in March, and then rose again. At Magadi the proportion of juveniles steadily rose to about 70% in April and May. The high proportion of young birds at Magadi seems to reflect the use of this area as a temporary staging area during passage, whereas Nakuru seems to accommodate a stable population from year to year. Of 410 males wintering in the southwestern part of the Netherlands, Castelijns *et al.* observed only 7% juveniles.

The proportion of juveniles is usually lower in the temperate moulting areas during the late summer than in the winter quarters in Africa somewhat later in the year. This can be partly explained by a shorter stay of juveniles in the moulting areas, and partly by alternative migration routes.

The age composition of these populations has been studied near Münster, West Germany, and in Friesland, the Netherlands. The proportion of juveniles among the birds present at the sewage-farms near Münster was about 11%, both among males and females, and was almost stable throughout the period of moult from the middle of June up to the beginning of October. The proportion of juveniles among the individuals passing through Münster was higher. Juvenile females stayed only 12 days in the area, and adult females on average 19 days. Juvenile males stayed about 27 days in the area, and adult males on average 35 days. Thus, approximately 18% of the females and 13% of the males passing through were juveniles. In Friesland and North Holland a similar proportion (11%) was found among the males present, but among the females this proportion was much higher (30%). The proportion of juveniles was lower at the beginning of the moulting period. The first juveniles arrive in Friesland by the end of July. Their proportion rises steadily up to the middle of September, and then remains fairly constant. Considering that females and juveniles stay a relatively short time in this area, the proportion of juveniles passing through Friesland seems to be higher than in Münster.

Sex-ratio

Another aspect of the dynamics of Ruff populations is the representation of the two sexes. In Roderwolde many males and only a few females returned at the end of March and the beginning of April. Around the end of April and the beginning of May, females could be present in very large groups which foraged in the area and visited the leks. Quite often their numbers greatly exceeded those of males visiting the leks. By the end of May most females had left the area and only a few stayed for nesting, though their numbers were considerably lower than those of the males displaying on leks.

In April and May 1979 I counted the number of males and females in flying groups in the Lauwersmeer area and observed an enormous increase in the proportion of females by the beginning of May. In the second third of April 1979 I saw 44 Ruffs in flying groups in this area. Only 16% of these individuals were females, and in the last 10 days of April this proportion was even lower, 13% of 165 individuals. In the first 10 days of May the proportion of females suddenly rose up to 64% of the 183 Ruffs counted, and finally in the second third up to 88% of 280 individuals (Figure 30A)!

The proportion of females caught by Klaas Koopman and his associates in Friesland and North Holland remained somewhat lower during spring. Yet it did rise from zero in the period from December till March, up to 54% during the first 10 days of May. In the late summer the proportion of females caught was about the same. It rose from 10% in the first 10 days of July up to 44% in the second third of August, and dropped again to 27% in the second third of October and to zero in the period from December till March (Figure 30B). Thus, the sex-ratio in the Dutch population of Ruffs is not constant, indicating that the timing of migration differs between the sexes.

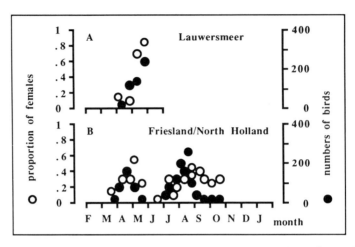

FIGURE 30 *The proportion of females (open dots) and total numbers of Ruffs (black dots) observed in the Lauwersmeer (A) and trapped for ringing in Friesland and North-Holland (B) in relation to time of year.*

In Roderwolde the population of breeding females seemed to be smaller than the population of males in the area, at least during the years in which I did my research. Data collected by Zomerdijk in the northwestern part of the Netherlands also suggest that the number of males on leks there is sometimes higher, but never lower, than the number of breeding females. In the Lauwersmeer area I got the impression that the number of males in the area was similar to, or perhaps somewhat higher than, the number of breeding females. The number of males on leks, however, was much lower than the number of breeding females, especially during the first years after enclosure. At Tipperne, in Denmark, Andersen counted almost equal numbers of males and females over a period of several years. The number of females, however, tended to fluctuate from year to year, whereas the number of males remained fairly constant. At the island of Kirr, in East Germany, Scheufler and Stiefel also found equal numbers of males and females. However, of 858 Ruffs caught during spring migration by Harengerd and his collaborators near Münster, 71% were females. The proportion of females seems to be still higher in Ruffs passing through Eber Gölü in Turkey early in April, where Alphons Van Winden and his collaborators observed 84% females among the 633 Ruffs counted. In Finland, females also seem to outnumber males. Two thirds of 14 000 birds ringed there were females! David Lank and Connie Smith counted about 70 males and 400 females (85%) per day during the second half of May and about 30 males and 30 females in June at Virkkula, near Oulu in northern Finland. The estimate for females during this last period might be too low, because many females were nesting at the time.

Somewhat more to the east on leks in Estonia and in the region of Leningrad, in the Soviet Union, Ivanova estimated the proportion of females at more than 75%. These figures suggest that, on average, females migrate further north for breeding than do males. However, data from the breeding quarters in Siberia to confirm this idea are lacking.

The proportion of males caught by Pearson in the winter quarters in Kenya varied between 0.7% and 11.5% at lake Nakuru, and between 3.5% and 15.3% at lake Magadi. Of a total of 1600 Ruffs caught by Schmitt and Whitehouse in South Africa only 7.5% were males. In western Africa, the proportion of males seems to be much higher: of 1988 birds caught by the OAG of Münster in Senegal 32% were males. In the northern winter quarters, males seem to be the more common sex. Of 57 Ruffs recovered in France during the winter, 88% were males. Of more than 4000 Ruffs wintering in the southwestern part of the Netherlands and the northwestern part of Belgium, 98% were classified as males by Castelijns and his associates. Thus, the proportion of males in wintering groups seems to increase from south to north.

The proportion of males in the moulting areas in western Europe seems to decrease from west to east. Of 845 Ruffs caught in summer and autumn in the northwestern part of the Netherlands by Pieters and his collaborators, about two thirds were males. In the catches by Koopman and collaborators in Friesland and North Holland, 68% of 1474 Ruffs were males. The catches in summer and autumn by Harengerd near Münster consisted of fewer males than females: 41% of 2786 individuals. This proportion was higher, however, than the proportion of males found during spring migration (29%). The relatively high proportion of males in the temperate moulting areas can be attributed to their staying longer for moulting. The adult males in Münster spend on average 35 days in the area, and at least 73% of them moult. Adult females spend on average only 19 days in the area, and about 59% moult. Moreover, most females interrupt moulting at an earlier stage than males.

Morphological features

Populations of Ruffs may be characterized by an unusual representation of birds with particular morphological features, such as large body measurements, or certain plumage types. In Section 2.5 the possible trend of increasing pro-portions of males with white plumage from southwest to northeast (see also Table 13) was discussed. Here, I only want to go briefly into the body-size of birds of different populations.

In the breeding populations there are indications of a trend for decreasing body measurements from south to north. Drenckhahn measured 19 skins of males from Swedish Lapland and 82 from western and central Europe, all collected during the breeding period. The Swedish birds had smaller wing and bill measurements than the birds of southern origin. This seems to conflict with

Bergmann's rule, which states that endothermic animals should be adapted to low temperatures in the north by large body measurements, because the favourable relation between volume and surface area lowers the loss of body heat. However, in the Ringed Plover, and some other waders, a similar exception to this rule has been explained by Salomonsen on the basis of the geographical distribution of these birds during the remaining part of the year. Birds from the southern breeding areas would stay close to their breeding quarters during the winter, and thus suffer rather low temperatures during their yearly cycle. In contrast, birds from the northern breeding areas would traverse the winter quarters of the former birds by so-called *leapfrog migration*, and winter more to the south under less severe climatic conditions. Similar circumstances might apply to the Ruff. An alternative explanation, however, will be given in Section 4.6.

Summary

Ruffs breed in northern Asia, and northern and northwestern Europe. They winter in Africa, and, in smaller numbers, in southern Asia and southern and western Europe. Stopovers on the way between between breeding grounds and winter quarters may be used by large groups of Ruffs for several weeks for foraging and moulting. Ruffs have a strong tendency to return to the same breeding grounds, wintering sites, and even moulting places. Yet some Ruffs may wander far away from their usual routes. Thus, considerable exchange between populations seems to exist. The composition of populations is not stable: it varies both between geographical regions and in the course of time. Juveniles tend to migrate further south for wintering. The following spring they may wander widely without paying much attention to the breeding grounds or may even spend the summer in the winter quarters. Females also tend to migrate far south for wintering, but to breed they go, on average, further north than males. Also, females spend less time than males in the moulting areas. There is some evidence that the proportion of males with white plumage in the breeding areas increases from southwest to northeast. Moreover, in the breeding areas body size seems to decrease from south to north.

4.2 DIET AND FORAGING

To meet their energy demands, Ruffs have a varied diet, as shown in several studies on the stomach contents of birds shot both in the breeding areas and elsewhere. In the most northern breeding areas the diet is rather uniform. Kistchinskij and Flint found that Ruffs in the deltas of the Jana and Indirga rivers in northeastern Siberia mainly fed on larval and adult midges (especially chironomids), crane flies and caddis flies. In June and early July their diet

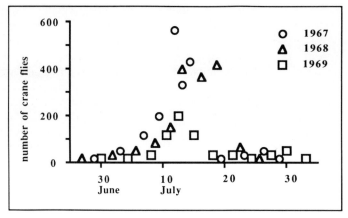

FIGURE 31 *The total catch per three days of adult crane flies near Barrow, Alaska, in three successive seasons (after MacLean and Pitelka, 1971).*

consisted mainly of larvae and pupae, in late July adult insects predominated, and in early August the Ruffs switched again to larvae. These changes seem to reflect the availability of the different kinds of prey. According to MacLean and Pitelka, adult crane flies in the tundra near Barrow (northern Alaska) are only available during a short period, lasting about 10 days, around the middle of July (Figure 31). Larvae and pupae are available for a longer period, from the beginning of June up to the beginning of September, but cannot be caught as easily as adults. Quite likely the situation in northern Siberia is comparable. Yet the tundra habitat is very important for the Ruff and many other species of birds. Kistchinskij calculated that the wet tundras around the river Ob, in north-western Siberia, produce about 18–35 kg of arthropods and worms per hectare per year. This production may supply enough food for 50–150 g of bird biomass (all tundra species lumped together). Thus, each reeve (without offspring) would need 0.8–2.5 ha only for herself, and each ruff 1.5–4.5 ha.

In more southerly breeding areas, and places used for resting during migration, the diet is much more diverse. Apart from the prey types mentioned above, Ruffs in these areas may also eat various kinds of flies, beetles, plant material, and, less often, molluscs and vertebrates such as small fish and tadpoles.

Data on the diet in tropical wintering areas have been collected by Bernard Tréca. These suggest that animal food is utilized if available, but, probably because of shortage, plant material, especially rice grains, also assumes great importance. In Senegal Ruffs forage in very large numbers on easily exploited rice spilled on the fields after harvest. In typical years the birds only need to forage for four hours per day, but much longer when rice is scarce.

Foraging Ruffs in non-breeding plumage (photo Joop Brinkkemper)

Foraging

Ruffs tend to forage in flocks, which are quite often large. This is most obvious in their winter quarters in Africa, during migration and on resting stopovers. Migrating and resting flocks may consist of several hundreds of individuals, and wintering groups of several thousands. Most often one sex predominates in a flock: usually, a flock, even a large one, is composed only of females or males, with mixing of the sexes being surprisingly rare. Foraging groups are also common in the breeding areas. Males who are not bound to a particular lek, and non-breeding females, forage together, sometimes in company with individuals who have not yet reached their breeding quarters. Lekking males tend to forage together, often leaving the lek together, and returning simultaneously. Nesting females, however, seem to forage alone.

In my own study area, near Roderwolde, I got the impression that Ruffs prefer to forage in a soft substrate, quite often in shallow water. Sometimes, in early spring, these favoured foraging areas became greatly enlarged through the action of the nearby pumping station. When this happened, huge flocks of Ruffs, probably migrants, could be seen foraging in the bed of the canal covered with shallow puddles and large areas of soft mud. In fact all the breeding areas I knew, especially the Lauwersmeer area, were characterized by the presence of soft substrates and vast areas of shallow water. The decline of the Ruff in some places is thus closely associated with draining and the consequent hardening of the substrate. Survival of Ruffs in other areas seems to depend on regular control of the water-table. Soft substrates and shallow waters also predominate in the northern breeding grounds on wet and moist tundras. Moreover, migrant groups also seem to prefer to rest in shallow waters with muddy eutrophic substrates, such as the sewage-farms of the factories making starch from potatoes, or cardboard from straw, and several such places, quite close to where I live, are frequently visited by Ruffs. The moulting area near Münster, for example, is an artificial complex of numerous sewage-farms, covering more than 500 ha, and formerly used to clean the city's effluent water.

Ruffs also forage in areas with short and sparse vegetation, such as grazed or short grasslands and wet and moist tundras. They avoid tall and dense vegetation, and also stony dry tundras, but may forage in large numbers in wet areas of low vegetation. I saw large groups of Ruffs foraging in meadow areas on several occasions, especially in early spring. For instance, on 21 April 1969 I saw two large foraging flocks, consisting of 460 males and only five females, in adjacent meadows, close to Zoutkamp, in the north of the Netherlands. In later years in early spring, I saw groups of a similar size, or even larger, on natural grasslands in the Lauwersmeer area. The earliest groups were almost purely male, while later in the year groups could be composed of females only. Cultivated and natural grasslands are also important foraging areas for the large groups of Ruffs which rest and moult in the Netherlands during summer and early autumn.

Food is generally found by sight or by touch. Ruffs may look around and peck at small prey visible on the surface of the mud, by the shoreline, or among the vegetation. They may also jab with their bills into the mud or other soft substrates to extract prey from below the surface. The birds often jab into substrates covered with shallow water and may completely immerse their heads. They may wade in the water, and occasionally even swim. Most foraging is characterized by restless moving, walking, and running, in various directions, while looking, pecking, or jabbing. Burton distinguished two types of jabs in calidridine sandpipers: *probing*, in which the whole bill is quietly inserted into the mud, and *stitching*, in which a very rapid series of jabs is made, usually very shallow and close together. Both methods are commonly used by Ruffs. Bolze has shown that the bills of snipe and calidridine sandpipers, including the Ruff, are well suited for detecting prey by probing and stitching. Their tips contain large numbers of tactile sense cells, the so-called Herbst corpuscles, which enable the bird to discover invisible prey, such as larval arthropods, worms, and small molluscs, below the surface of the mud.

Summary

The diet of the Ruff on the northern breeding grounds is uniform and consists of larval and adult midges and other dipterids. On the southern breeding grounds and moulting places the diet is more diverse, but consists almost entirely of animal food. In the tropical winter quarters, plant food, especially rice, is also important. Except for nesting females, Ruffs typically forage in flocks. They prefer soft substrates and shallow water for foraging, especially sewage-farms, wet tundras, meadows, and natural grasslands. Prey is found by sight, but also by means of small tactile sense cells in the bill tip. Invisible prey are located by two methods: probing and stitching.

4.3 MOULT

The renewal of feathers requires particular nutrients. This may imply extra food for the bird, and thus extra time spent foraging. Adult male Ruffs moult three times every year, which is exceptional among birds. The first accurate description of the moulting process was given by Detlev Drenckhahn on the basis of skins of Ruffs shot or found in OstFriesland and Schleswig Holstein, West Germany. Some of these birds were probably breeders, but many others were migrants resting in the area. More details about autumn and winter moulting emerged from studies by Schmitt and Whitehouse, and by Pearson on Ruffs trapped in the wintering areas in South Africa and Kenya. Further information on the main moult in summer was collected by Michael Harengerd close to Münster, West Germany, and by Klaas Koopman in Friesland, the Netherlands. Schmitt and Whitehouse, Pearson, Harengerd, and Koopman were all able to relate body weight to the stage of moult. The latter three also succeeded in recapturing individuals, or even in following colour-marked individuals over a longer period. This offered a better insight into the temporal pattern of moult. Here I shall give only a concise description of the moulting process itself. A summary is presented in Figure 32.

Adults

Adult males and females undergo a complete moult after the breeding season. Males and non-breeding females may start in June, breeding females three to four weeks later. Head and ruff feathers are the first to be renewed, followed by the other small body or contour feathers. *Post-breeding moult* is concluded with renewal of the large flight feathers, although not all at the same time. Primary moult proceeds in a strict sequence from the innermost towards the outermost pinion. A complete moult may last approximately three months, but longer when it occurs in the winter quarters. Both Harengerd and Koopman calculated that wing moult lasts at least two months. Moult of the first small feathers usually starts in the breeding area. Wing-moult may also start in the breeding areas, but birds from northern populations, in particular the breeding females, start moulting in special resting areas, or in their winter quarters. An individual may stay in the same area throughout the whole wing-moulting process or it may interrupt wing-moult ('suspended moult') for migration. Then, its wings are characterized by a complete set of full-grown pinions, the inner parts of both rows of primaries being renewed, and the outer parts still consisting of old feathers.

Some male Ruffs from southern populations may even complete wing moult

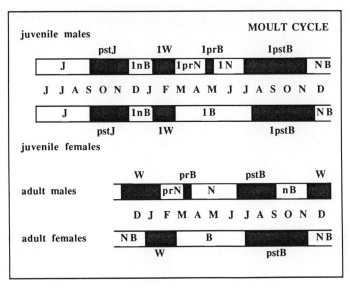

FIGURE 32 *The yearly cycle of moulting in adult and juvenile males and females of the Ruff. Plumages (open): J, juvenile; (1)nB, (first) non-breeding; (1)prN, (first) prenuptial; (1)N, (first) nuptial; (1)B, (first) breeding. Moults (filled): pstJ, postjuvenile; (1)W, (first) winter; (1)prB, (first) pre-breeding; (1)pstB, (first) post-breeding.*

in their breeding areas. Other males and non-breeding females may complete it in the resting areas, but many males and almost all females, especially those who have been breeding, seem to complete wing-moult in their winter quarters. By the beginning of September the first males, along with a few, probably non-breeding, females, have completed their moult. Many more females, probably breeders, complete their moult from the end of September onwards. Early completion only occurs in the breeding and resting areas. In the winter quarters moulting is somewhat delayed. Almost all males have finished moulting by the end of November and almost all females by the beginning of January. Post-breeding moult furnishes the birds with their *non-breeding plumage* which is rather pale without clear contrasts. The feathers on the back and the mantle have dark-grey centres and fairly broad, light fringes, giving the bird a scaly appearance. The feathers on the breast, flanks and belly are very light. There may be slight differences between individuals, especially in the throat region and the upper parts of the breast. Some individuals have conspicuous white parts in these areas, while others are much darker. All adult satellite males in our aviary were characterized by white throats in autumn and winter, whereas all independent males had fairly dark throats. Thus, it seems as if the satellite males can be distinguished from independent males throughout the year.

Male Ruff in non-breeding plumage (photo Joop Brinkkemper)

From November to March, males and females renew most of the head and body feathers, wing coverts, and tertials. The main flight feathers, the primaries and secondaries, of the adult birds are not renewed. Males start a few weeks before females, and also finish a few weeks earlier. *Winter moult* occurs mainly in the winter quarters and lasts approximately eight weeks. It supplies the female *breeding plumage*, in males also known as the *prenuptial plumage*. This plumage is darker than the non-breeding plumage, and shows more contrast. The feathers of back and mantle give a high-contrast scaly appearance to the bird. Breast, flanks and neck are spotted with small dark-grey or brownish patches. Sexual variation in plumage is almost non-existent. Variation between individuals, however, is considerable. This partly reflects the status of a bird. All satellite males in our experimental groups had large white areas in the head, throat, or upper-breast region, whereas none of the independent males had such characteristics. Males returning early in spring to the lekking area may still be in prenuptial plumage. Somewhat later in the courtship season, when most resident males have established residences, leks may also be visited by males with prenuptial plumage, the so-called naked-nape males, who may alternate between independent and satellite behaviour (see p. 49).

From the beginning of March up to the beginning of May, males renew head, breast, neck, flank, and many other small body feathers. *Pre-breeding moult* may start and proceed in the resting areas, but also in the breeding area. Many males conclude pre-breeding moult in their breeding area. Within one or two weeks they develop their *nuptial plumage*. The grey and brownish prenuptial feathers are exchanged for brilliantly coloured nuptial ones, arranged as a collar with two head-tufts and with many other special characteristics. The feathering around the base of the bill disappears, and the yellow, orange or red wattles become visible. Variation between individuals increases dramatically (see Section 2.5). Females also seem to renew some feathers during the pre-breeding moult period, but their new feathers do not differ from those developed during winter moult. Moreover, females do not show a clear discontinuity in the renewal of feathers between late winter and spring. Therefore, moult in adult females is best described as comprising one complete and one partial plumage generation per year, whereas adult males annually muster one complete and two partial plumage generations.

Juveniles

During their first week of life young Ruffs are downy and have no real feathers. Development of the first feathers lasts several weeks. Primaries are full-grown at about 50 days. The *juvenile plumage* resembles the adult non-breeding plumage, except that the dark parts on the back and mantle are darker and the crown of the head has black or very dark markings. Age can also be determined from the characteristics of single feathers. Juvenile mantle feathers, scapulars, tertials, tail feathers, and upper wing coverts are grey, and darker towards the tips with contrasting light fringes not found in adults. From the end of August, juveniles start to partly renew their body plumage, though not the main flight feathers. The inner main tail feathers or *retrices* may be renewed, but the outer retrices are retained along with some of the juvenile body feathers. By the end of December this *post-juvenile moult* is finished and the birds possess their *first non-breeding plumage*. It can be distinguished from the adult non-breeding plumage by the presence of juvenile characteristics, such as the contrastingly fringed outer retrices and upper wing coverts.

The *first winter moult* proceeds at the same time and in the same areas as winter moult in adults, but with slight differences: renewal of the small feathers is less complete in juveniles, but, in contrast to the adults, a small proportion of juveniles also renew the outer primaries. The *first breeding plumage* (or *first prenuptial plumage* in males) differs from the adult breeding plumage by the presence of some juvenile feathers (especially all, or almost all, heavily worn flight feathers and the outer retrices), some post-juvenile feathers, and first winter moult feathers. Yearling males may also undergo a *first pre-breeding moult*, especially when they return to the breeding areas. Usually their *first nuptial plumage* develops somewhat later than the nuptial plumage in adults, and with smaller feathers. Underdeveloped nuptial plumage, worn flight feathers and juvenile outer retrices still betray their age. They may mostly be recognized by the colour of their legs and bills, which are usually grey to greenish or brownish, compared to yellow, orange or pink in adults. Plumage differences between yearlings and adults disappear by the *first post-breeding moult*. This moult usually starts somewhat later than the post-breeding moult in adults, but apart from that it proceeds similarly.

Summary

Adult male Ruffs moult three times every year: (1) post-breeding moult during the summer and autumn, involving the whole plumage, and producing the non-breeding plumage; (2) winter moult, involving most of the plumage, but not the large flight feathers, and producing the breeding or prenuptial plumage; and (3) pre-breeding moult during the early spring, involving head, breast, and many small body feathers, and producing the nuptial plumage. In adult females winter moult and pre-breeding moult merge into one another, and cannot be considered as separate processes. Juvenile Ruffs have their juvenile plumage until their first autumn. Post-juvenile moult involves most of the body plumage, but only part of the flight feathers. It produces the first non-breeding plumage, which is replaced during winter by the first winter moult, which may involve the outer primaries. Both the first prenuptial and the first nuptial plumage can still be distinguished from adult plumages. The differences between yearlings and adults disappear after the first post-breeding moult during summer and autumn.

4.4 MIGRATION

The breeding areas of the Ruff, especially those in the far north, produce lots of food in late spring and summer, but almost nothing in autumn and winter. The migratory resting areas, which are also used for wing-moult, produce food in spring, summer and autumn, but are unsuitable for living in during most winters. The wintering areas produce food all the year round, but do not offer the right conditions for breeding. In order to exploit all these areas, the Ruff has to be able to migrate, moving periodically from one area to another. Since winter quarters in Africa and southern Asia are about 4500–15 000 km from the breeding areas, some Ruffs may travel more than 20 000 km per year.

Migration routes

Our knowledge of the flyways of Ruffs is mainly based on data concerning the presence of birds in different areas at different times of the year, and on recoveries of ringed birds. The general temporal and spatial distribution of Ruffs has been discussed already (Section 4.1). Now, I want to concentrate on ringing recoveries, based mainly on an extensive analysis by Gabriëlle Van Dinteren of the Euring data files, on the recoveries of birds ringed by Pearson in Kenya, on recoveries of those ringed by the OAG of Münster, and on correspondence with members of this group.

The migration patterns of Ruffs can be subdivided into two main systems. The birds from northwestern Europe tend to winter in western Africa. Of 678 recoveries of birds ringed in northwestern Europe (Britain, Belgium, the Netherlands, West Germany, East Germany, Poland, Denmark, Norway, Sweden, and Finland), 10 originate from northwestern Africa (Morocco, Algeria, and Tunisia), 45 from western Africa (Mauritania, Senegal, Guinea-Bissau, Mali, and Nigeria), and only two from the other African countries. In contrast, birds from Siberia tend to winter in southern Asia, but also in eastern, southern, and western Africa. Correspondingly, none of the 15 recoveries of birds ringed by Pearson in Kenya occurred in northwestern Europe. One was recovered in India, and all the others in the Soviet Union, mainly between 70°E and 155°E. Similarly, 17 Ruffs ringed in India were recovered in Siberia, mainly between 105°E and 150°E. The hypothesis that the Siberian populations also visit western African wintering grounds is based on recoveries in Siberia of birds ringed in Senegal and Nigeria.

As well as the overlapping winter quarters in western Africa, the breeding populations of northwestern Europe and Siberia also seem to show a considerable overlap of their flyways. This can be illustrated by the data on recoveries of birds ringed in summer and autumn (from July to December) in the moulting areas in western Europe. During the breeding season, birds moulting in Holland, north of Amsterdam, and ringed mainly by Pieters and his co-workers, were recovered in Denmark, Scandinavia, Finland, Poland and the Soviet Union (as far away as eastern Siberia). During the winter they were recovered mainly in France and western Africa (Senegal and Mali), and a few were recovered in Spain and Britain. Thus, it seems as if, in autumn, at least some eastern birds join the western birds on their way to western African winter quarters. The birds moulting near Münster, ringed by Harengerd and his associates, display a similar pattern. During the breeding season these Ruffs were recovered from Poland and the Soviet Union, two being found near the Kolyma river, about 170°E. In the latter region, two Ruffs ringed in India were also found, along with three ringed in South Africa. During the winter most of the birds ringed in Münster were recovered in northern and western Africa, many in western France, a few in Italy, but none in eastern and southern Africa.

The birds breeding in Siberia and wintering in India and eastern and southern Africa seem to follow the same routes in spring and summer, whereas the main flyways of birds wintering in western Africa might differ on the outward and return journeys. The monthly patterns of recoveries and the recovery data of birds ringed in the moulting areas in western Europe certainly suggest that this is the case.

The yearly recovery pattern is summarized in Table 21. It seems that most Ruffs from northern and western Europe and perhaps some from northern Asia return to their breeding grounds via Italy. Fewer Ruffs seem to take an alternative route across France. In fact many of the Ruffs recovered in early spring in France may have spent the winter in that country. In August and September a short migration wave proceeds over France. Somewhat later, in September and October, Italy experiences a probably smaller wave. In the same period considerable numbers of Ruffs are still present in the resting and moulting areas in western Europe. Yet one gets the impression from counts in the African winter quarters that most birds return to these areas from August to December. An influx of wintering Ruffs in France occurs in December, when conditions in western Europe deteriorate. Thus, spring migration seems to proceed mainly over Italy, whereas in autumn a more westerly route over France is preferred.

Ruffs ringed from July to December in North Holland showed a similar recovery pattern. Recoveries from early spring were mainly in Italy, and to a smaller extent in Belgium and France. However, the possibility cannot be excluded that these latter birds were wintering. The recoveries from autumn and winter were mainly in France, western Africa, and Spain. During this period none were recovered in Italy. The birds ringed in Münster were also found in Italy and southern France during spring migration, and, in much lower numbers, in western France and Spain. During autumn and winter many of these birds were found in the Netherlands, France, and western Africa. Only a few recoveries from this period were in Italy. Different flyways in spring and autumn are also suggested by the recoveries in the breeding season of the birds ringed during spring migration and the birds ringed in the wing-moult period. Birds ringed in spring near Münster tended to breed in the north (Scandinavia, Finland, and the regions bordering in Russia, and Estonia), whereas the birds ringed in autumn tended to breed in the east (Poland, Belorussia, Russia, and northern Siberia).

The analysis of recovery data, however, requires considerable caution. The probability that a bird is ringed at a particular place depends on its own activity and on the activity of ringers. The tendency of birds to concentrate in large flocks in particular areas encourages ringers. The probability of a bird being recovered at a particular place depends on hunting pressure, on the density of potential discoverers of dead birds, and on the likelihood of rings found being properly reported. Consequently the numbers of birds in the Euring data files, ringed and recovered in the different months of the year, vary enormously (Figure 33). Ringing occurred from July to September, especially in August, during summer migration and moult. Also, reasonable numbers were ringed in May during spring migration. Most birds were ringed in Finland, Sweden, Norway, Denmark, the Netherlands, and West Germany, all countries where Ruffs may concentrate during migration. Recoveries occurred mostly in March during early spring migration, and in August and September during late summer migration and moult. Most birds were recovered in Italy, the Soviet Union, France, Denmark and western Africa, mainly because of the hunting pressure in these countries.

Table 21 The distribution of recoveries over various regions during the different months of the year (after Van Dinteren).

	Jan.	Feb.	March	April	May	June	July	Aug.	Sept.	Oct.	Nov.	Dec.
Total number:	49	74	314	68	105	31	38	166	136	50	23	47
Percentage in:												
SU	4	0	0	3	43	55	13	33	19	12	0	0
SC	0	0	0	0	11	6	13	16	8	2	0	0
DK	0	0	0	3	24	26	8	24	10	10	4	0
CE	2	0	1	13	14	3	29	8	7	8	13	6
FR	59	27	13	6	0	0	16	12	17	20	39	68
IT	8	36	80	66	6	0	16	5	19	34	17	9
WQ	27	36	6	9	1	10	5	2	4	14	26	17

Key: N, total number; SU, Soviet Union including Siberia; SC, Norway, Sweden, Finland; DK, Denmark; CE, central and western Europe – Poland, East and West Germany, the Netherlands, Great Britain, Ireland, and Belgium; FR, mainly France, but also Spain and Portugal; IT, mainly Italy, but also Austria, Switzerland, Hungary, Rumania, Bulgaria, Yugoslavia, Greece, Turkey, and Cyprus; WQ, winter quarters – Africa and India.

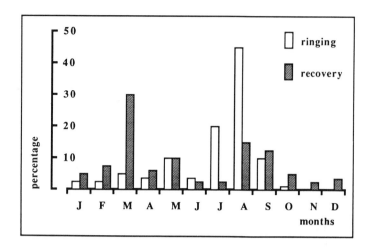

FIGURE 33 *The frequency of ringing (open columns) and recovery (filled columns) of Ruffs in different months of the year.*

The hypothesis that Ruffs breeding in northwestern Europe use different migration routes in spring and autumn cannot be supported by counts of resting groups in western Europe during both migration periods. The number of birds passing in the two periods seems to be the same. Moreover, data collected by the OAG of Münster on birds wintering in Senegal do not support this idea either. These birds were marked in their winter quarters using picric acid to produce yellow patches on their feathers. Sightings during the spring migration of these dye-marked birds were concentrated in western Europe: the Netherlands, Britain, France, and West Germany; they were relatively rare in Italy and central Europe, and very rare in eastern Europe, although extensive numbers of migrating Ruffs were observed in these latter areas (40 000–55 000). Thus, the differences between spring and autumn in recovery patterns might only reflect differences in hunting pressure through the year.

The main flyways of the Ruffs are summarized in Figure 34. Although several thousands of ringed Ruffs have been recovered, the data do not allow conclusions regarding the fine details of the migration pattern. This may be illustrated by the following example. Observations on the age distribution and the sex-ratio in different breeding and wintering populations of the Ruff (see Section 4.1) strongly suggest that juveniles migrate later and further south than adults, and that females migrate further than males. However, it is impossible to confirm these trends from the relatively few recoveries in the winter quarters. Similarly, recovery data are too poor to draw any conclusions about a possible relationship between the latitudes of the breeding and wintering areas. We need

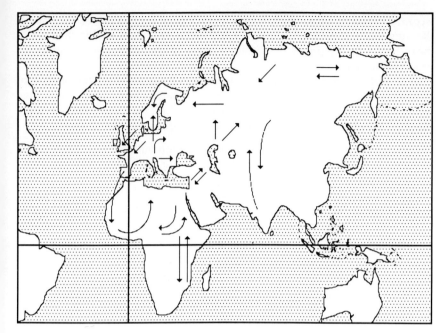

FIGURE 34 *The main flyways of the Ruff.*

further data to unravel such details. An attempt to arrive at some answers empirically will be made below.

Energy considerations in migration

Within the Ruff's group of close relatives, the calidridine sandpipers, long-distance migrations are typical of species with polygamous or promiscuous mating systems, and also of species in which one parent performs all or most of the parental care. Most monogamous species with biparental care winter much closer to their breeding areas. J.P. Myers has interpreted this relationship between migration distance and parental care pattern and mating system by assuming that long migration distances select for early departure. This may lead to the development of behavioural strategies for single parental care, which then would facilitate the evolution of non-monogamous mating systems. Ruffs indeed seem to leave the breeding area as early as possible, staying no longer than necessary for reproduction or growth. Males and non-breeding females leave these areas by the end of June, while breeding females stay three to four weeks longer until their young are independent. Juveniles stay another couple of weeks. This ample time-schedule may be important for minimizing the risks of the long journey ahead. Moreover, early departure might enable the bird to make use of highly productive foraging areas in the temperate countries for processes such as wing-moult.

Male Ruffs tend to winter further north than females. This phenomenon of dissimilar distributions of the two sexes is known from other calidridine sandpipers and also from unrelated species. J.P. Myers considered three different hypotheses to explain this latitudinal segregation of the sexes:

— the larger sex might be able to dominate the smaller sex on the foraging grounds, and thus force the smaller sex to migrate further;
— the larger sex might be able to tolerate harsher climates, and thus stay closer to the breeding grounds than the smaller sex;
— there might be a selective premium for one sex to arrive as early as possible on the breeding grounds, for instance to establish a high-quality territory, and thus to winter as close as possible to this area.

The first and the second hypotheses can be eliminated, because in certain species the smaller sex winters closer to the breeding grounds. The third hypothesis cannot be rejected on this basis, and may be valid for the Ruff, although a fourth mechanism seems to play a major role. After breeding, the sex which is able to return early enough to the safe and highly productive temperate foraging areas may complete wing-moult close to the breeding grounds (see Section 4.5). But the sex which has to stay with the young arrives too late in those areas to find enough food, or a sufficiently mild climate, to complete wing-moult and has, thus, to migrate further south. To summarize, an unequal share of parental duties among the sexes may be associated with relatively short migration distances in the sex performing little or no parental care. Relatively long migration distances may be forced upon the sex performing most parental care. In contrast, similar migration distances of the sexes would be expected in species in which male and female share parental duties equally.

Migration requires a considerable expenditure of energy, and thus extra food. Moreover, to traverse long distances, the bird needs good plumage, and especially good flight feathers. The long trip from the breeding area to the winter quarters, or the return trip to the breeding area, may be interrupted for several days, weeks, or even months, for building up new fat reserves and also for moulting. Such resting, foraging, and moulting areas may be visited year after year, though Ruffs seem to behave rather flexibly during migration and wintering. They tend to stay when food is sufficient, and to move to other areas when conditions become adverse.

Ruffs store lots of fat before departing for distant destinations. About 40% of their body weight may consist of directly metabolizable fat reserves: 110 g in males and 60 g in females. Thus, males may reach body weights around 260 g, compared with lean weights of only about 150 g, and females may reach 150 g, compared with lean weights around 90 g. Klaas Koopman has calculated that this amount of fat can produce energy sufficient for one non-stop flight, lasting about three days, from the moulting areas in the Netherlands along the coastline to the wintering areas in Senegal and Mali about 4500 km away. It is quite likely that the birds do really make such long flights in the late summer, since at this time they may have great difficulty finding other foraging areas suitable for replenishing their fat reserves on the way.

Weights over 220 g in males and 130 g in females have been recorded during the late summer in the moulting areas. In the breeding areas males maintain body weights around 190 g, and females around 110 g. In the eastern African winter quarters, body weights are still lower: about 170 g in males and 100 g in females, except by the time of departure north, when body weights (in eastern Africa) reach the same values as in the breeding areas. This is not sufficient to make a non-stop flight over several thousands of kilometres. Therefore, northward migration of Ruffs wintering in southern and eastern Africa and breeding in Siberia has to proceed in fairly short hops, using several foraging areas *en route* to replenish their reserves. They go north via the East African Rift Valley, through Sudan, thus avoiding very long stretches of desert. The Ruffs may cross Turkey or Iraq, and rest at the northern coast of the Caspian Sea before departing for their breeding areas. This last stop is probably important for building up the reserves necessary for long trips to the Siberian breeding quarters, which are still 1500–6500 km away. An alternative route to the breeding grounds in the northeastern parts of Siberia would cross southern Arabia, southern Iran, and Afghanistan. Such a route, however, only seems to be possible with considerable fat reserves, since the birds would have to traverse a wide desert region, unsuitable for foraging.

Many Ruffs from the western African winter quarters seem to route through Italy on their way to the breeding areas in northwestern Europe. The distance between the inundation zones of the Niger in Mali and the area around the Po river in Italy is approximately 3500 km. If Ruffs can find the food to store enough fat in these winter quarters, this distance may be traversed in one non-stop flight, lasting about two days. Data collected by the OAG of Münster on Ruffs wintering in Senegal suggest that this option is feasible, and that it might even represent the normal pattern. At the beginning of March the males in this area increase their body weight up to the values reached in Friesland before departing in late summer. This amount of fat seems to be sufficient for the Ruffs to reach western and central Europe. Moreover, Ruffs dyed in Senegal have been sighted in central and western Europe: northern Italy, France, and the Netherlands; but not in southern countries, such as Tunisia and Spain, in spite of extensive observations in the wetlands of these areas. This would imply that Ruffs wintering in western Africa have a different strategy for migrating to their breeding grounds from those wintering in eastern Africa. After reaching Italy, Ruffs may proceed in rather short stages from one resting area to another. There are many suitable foraging areas available in early spring and the distances between them are not very great. The Ruffs rarely stay long in these resting areas. They do not need to build up large fat reserves to reach the next stopovers, such as the sewage-farms near Münster, or the Waddensea area. The final resting areas, used before the last flight to the north, may be visited for a longer period, suggesting that they are important for the production of pre-breeding fat reserves. Harengerd has shown that body weights of Ruffs resting near Münster increase considerably during the Ruff's stay in early spring. The males arriving by the end of March and the beginning of April weigh around 180 g, but have increased to 220 g by the time they leave in the middle of May. Similarly, female body weight increases from about 115 g at the beginning of April to about 125 g by the middle of May. The body weights of individuals recaptured at the end of the stopover can be found to have increased by more than 30%!

For the northern breeding populations, the beginning of the summer and autumn migration seems to proceed in rather short hops. In many Ruffs, especially males, wing-moult starts somewhere on their way from the breeding to the wintering grounds, usually in the moulting areas. During moult in western Europe, the birds maintain normal body weights: about 185 g in males and 120 g in females. Non-moulting birds and the birds who have interrupted wing-moult (suspended moult) reach much higher body weights: about 230 g or more in males and about 140 g in females. These are probably the birds ready to migrate further to their wintering areas.

Summary

Ruffs from northwestern Europe tend to winter in western Africa and those from Siberia in southern and eastern Africa, in India, and also in western Africa. Both breeding populations also have partly overlapping flyways. Ruffs from Siberia seem to follow the same migration routes in spring and autumn. Recovery data on the Ruffs breeding or moulting in western Europe suggest that the main route for spring migration crosses Italy, whereas the main route for autumn migration is further west, across France. However, counts in resting areas and sightings of dye-marked Ruffs do not support such a difference. Male Ruffs tend to winter further north than females. This might be explained by the reproductive advantages for males arriving early on the breeding grounds, but also by the fact that males, in contrast to most females, meet the conditions for completing post-breeding moult close to the breeding areas. Flight distances are restricted by fat reserves. The maximum distances which can be traversed in a non-stop flight are of the order of 4000 km. The Ruffs resting in western Europe in the summer and autumn probably reach their winter quarters in western Africa in one non-stop flight. They also seem to return to these resting areas in one single flight. The birds wintering in eastern and southern Africa seem to make more, but shorter, flights to reach their breeding grounds.

4.5 Costs and time-schedules

Every year a Ruff flies from its winter quarters to its breeding grounds, and back again. In the meantime it renews its feathers, some of them several times, and also spends time on reproduction. Here I want to consider the timing of these various activities and make some calculations about the total time needed to perform them all. The main reason for this is to investigate to what extent time limits the Ruff's behavioural options.

Reproductive investments consist of egg-production, incubation, parental care, and lekking. Females produce four eggs, weighing altogether about 80 g, which are incubated for about three weeks. The young are tended for another two weeks. In rich foraging areas, such as the sewage farms near Münster, Harengerd observed that during spring the body weight of a female may increase by 5 g per day. If this value is a reasonable reflection of the bird's intake abilities in the breeding area, and if this intake fully contributes to egg mass, then the production of four eggs would take about 16 days. In that case females would need to invest about seven weeks in reproduction. Males, in the southern breeding areas, may also spend about seven weeks on leks, compared with less than three weeks in the northern breeding areas.

The time-costs of migration are made up of the time needed to traverse the distance, and the time needed to build up the fat reserves to be metabolized during migration. Assuming, like Harengerd and Koopman, that Ruffs maintain air speeds around 70 km h^{-1}, the birds may traverse about 1700 km per day, or 12 000 km per week. The males, who are relatively heavy, need more fat to traverse a given distance than the females. Similarly, the individuals with ample fat reserves need more energy to fly than the lighter individuals with only small reserves. Using Davidson's formula, and the assumptions presented by Klaas Koopman, I calculated that a female departing with a body weight including the maximum of 40% stored fat is able to convert every gram of fat into a flight range of 74 km. When she starts with 20% of fat, she may achieve 78 km per gram of fat, and when she starts with only 10% of fat, every gram is converted into 83 km. Males departing with fat reserves amounting to 40% of their body weight convert every gram into a flight range of 49 km, or 55 km when starting with 20% of fat, or 58 km with only 10% of fat. In spring, at the sewage-farms near Münster, Harengerd found that females were able to store up to 5 g of fat per day, and males up to 4 g. During the late summer, females produced up to the same amount, 5 g per day, but males were able to double their spring rate of fat production, up to 8 g per day. These figures are maxima in a highly productive foraging area and it is very likely that much less can be gained in most other foraging areas visited before, during, and after migration. However, these are the only reasonable data on the rate of fat production, and thus they tempt some further speculations. They may offer a basis for calculating the minimal time-cost for spring and autumn migration in females and in males: the sum of the time needed for fat production and the time needed for flight. My calculations are based on the costs for birds starting with the maximal amount of fat (40%). I considered four different populations:

(1)   The Dutch breeding population, wintering in Senegal and Mali, about 4500 km away from the breeding grounds.
(2)   The population breeding in northern Scandinavia, also wintering in western Africa, at a distance of about 7000 km.
(3)   The population breeding in western Siberia, assumed also to winter in western Africa, about 8500 km away.
(4)   A hypothetical population breeding in the easternmost areas of Siberia (eastern Chukotka) and wintering about 15 000 km away in southern Africa.

The minimal time-costs of migration, calculated in weeks, for these four populations are given in Table 22A. Under ideal conditions females breeding in the Netherlands may spend only four weeks per year on migration. Under similar conditions males breeding in eastern Chukotka and wintering in southern Africa would migrate for not less than 19 weeks per year!

The first stages of post-breeding moult may occur in the breeding areas and during the first stages of summer migration. Renewal of some of the small body feathers may be combined with care of the offspring or with short-distance flights in the direction of moulting places and wintering areas. Consequently, the time-costs of renewal of the small body feathers are low during summer. The time needed for wing-moult in the late summer moulting areas in western Europe have been estimated by Harengerd at 60–70 days, and by Koopman at 72 days, in both cases approximately 10 weeks. Many birds, however, especially females, moult their flight feathers in Africa, where the time-costs seem to be much higher. Pearson estimated that wing-moult in Kenya lasted 110–130 days, approximately 17 weeks. This long duration may be due to a change of diet in the winter quarters (see Section 4.2). Frequent interruptions of winter moult in these areas also suggest that moulting places high demands on the birds. Winter moult lasts about eight weeks in both sexes, and prenuptial moult in males lasts about two weeks. Thus, the total time-costs of moult amount to 25 weeks in most females, and 20 weeks in most males.

The total time-costs (under ideal circumstances) of reproduction, migration and moult for the males and the females of the four populations are summarized in Table 22B. From the assumptions above, males in the northern breeding areas have lower time-costs than females for reproduction, apparently higher time-costs for migration, and usually lower time-costs for moult. Overall, the table shows that males consequently have lower time-costs than females. The difference between males and females may, in practice, be even more pronounced, since males tend to winter closer to their breeding areas than females. However, the table further shows that even the females who hypothetically breed in eastern Chukotka and winter in southern Africa should be able to

Table 22 (A) The minimum time (in weeks) needed to build up reserves and to fly from the winter quarters to the breeding grounds and back again; (B) minimum estimates for the time-costs (in weeks) per year of reproduction, migration, and moult for males and females.

	NL	SC	WS	ES
A.				
Spring migration:				
Males	4	6	7	12
Females	2	3	4	7
Summer migration:				
Males	2	3	4	7
Females	2	3	4	7
B.				
Reproduction:				
Males	7	4	3	3
Females	7	7	7	7
Migration:				
Males	6	9	11	19
Females	4	6	8	14
Moult:				
Males	20	20	20	20
Females	25	25	25	25
Total time needed:				
Males	33	33	34	42
Females	36	38	40	46

Key: NL, breeding in the Netherlands, wintering in western Africa; SC, breeding in northern Scandinavia, wintering in western Africa; WS, breeding in western Siberia, wintering in western Africa; ES, breeding in eastern Siberia, wintering in southern Africa.

manage their complete programme during the 52 weeks of the year, at least under ideal circumstances.

The higher time-costs for females are due to reproduction, longer distances between the breeding grounds and the winter quarters, and the fact that they moult their flight feathers in the winter quarters. In view of the conclusion that the female's time budget is tight, one might wonder why females migrate further than males, and why they usually moult in the winter quarters. To answer this question, one has to consider the timing of the female's breeding investments, the availability of food in the temperate resting areas, and the climatological conditions in these regions. Most females leave the breeding area later than males. Early in summer, food may be abundant in the resting areas but may decline later on. Moreover, the weather also deteriorates as autumn approaches. Moulting of the body feathers leads to reduced insulation, and thus to increased costs of maintaining body temperature.

Birds which leave early are thus able to undergo the whole process of wing-moult, and to build up enough fat to reach their winter quarters. Later birds do not have this option. They may manage to complete wing-moult, but must then winter closer to the resting area, or, alternatively, may interrupt wing-moult to produce fat for migration. The first possibility is somewhat risky; the second one is a trade-off against the time-budget, because completion of wing-moult takes more time in the winter quarters. Those birds leaving much later in summer may be unable to start wing-moult at all in the resting areas. The only option they have is to build up fat for migration, and to moult in the winter quarters. Thus, at the time of the female's departure, the temperate resting areas are no longer suitable for moulting. This seems to be the main reason why females migrate further than males.

Summary

On the basis of data on time budgets, rates of fat deposition in the resting areas, and flight costs, I was able to calculate the time needed to complete reproduction, migration, and moult for Ruffs from different geographical regions. The time costs of reproduction amount to seven weeks for reeves and three to seven weeks for ruffs under ideal conditions. The minimum time-costs of migration vary between four weeks in reeves nesting in the Netherlands and wintering in western Africa, and 19 weeks in ruffs displaying in eastern Siberia and wintering in southern Africa. Minimum time-costs of moult vary between 20 weeks in males and 25 weeks in females. The female's time-schedule seems to be more tight than the male's.

4.6 DO FEMALES NEST NEAR THE LEKS WHICH THEY VISIT?

In 1977, several years after finishing my thesis on the behaviour of male Ruffs, I heard a talk by Jack Bradbury on his ideas relating home ranges of females to the distribution of leks in African fruit bats. His model was based mainly on theoretical considerations. He took the line that the formation of leks only pays males if females prefer aggregations to dispersed males, and, further, large aggregations over small ones. In addition, leks should be distributed in such a way that all females are able to copulate, and thus that the average copulation score per male is maximal. The model predicted that in a large expanse of suitable and uniform habitat the distances between leks should be equal to the diameter of the home range of a female plus two times the distance over which females are able to detect leks. In such a situation lek size is maximal, provided that all females are able to find a lek. He tested the model by measuring the home ranges of radio-tagged females, by estimating the detection ranges of the leks of these noisy bats, and by measuring the distances between leks. The fit of the data on fruit bats to the model appeared to be good. However, the model was meant to be general for other lekking species and this prompted me to test its value for the Ruff. In fact, the model offered a new direction for my work on the Ruff.

The leks in my study area and its wide surroundings were far from regularly distributed. Some of them were very close together, such as leks A and B, and also the other leks near Roderwolde. However, the distances between leks could be much larger. For instance, those near Roderwolde and those near Boerakker and Sebaldeburen were about 13 km apart, although the area in between seemed to be equally suitable for breeding. The leks of Ruffs seem to be distributed in clusters (see Section 2.1). The distances between leks within clusters are of the order of 100–1000 m, while the distances between clusters are of the order of 10 km. This does not fit with Bradbury's model, unless the

clusters are considered as the relevant units. This possibility is reasonable because the distances between leks in the same cluster seem to fall within the detection range of flying females, whereas the distances between clusters are much larger.

Another problem arose when I tried to estimate the size of the female's home range. Early in spring large groups of females may visit an area for a few minutes, a few hours, or a few days. I cannot say much about the movements of those groups, but they are very unlikely to stay within an area of a few square kilometres in the course of a week. Judging from their activity, they seem to fly distances more like ten or tens of kilometres, perhaps even more. Since many females seem to visit the Dutch lekking areas on migration, the flight range might be hundreds or perhaps thousands of kilometres in the course of a month. In contrast, the females who breed in the area seem to move within a restricted range with a radius of a few hundred metres around their nests. Thus, the size of a female's home range is flexible and depends on whether she is migrating to her breeding grounds, exploring an area for a nesting site, or actually occupying a nest. The home range concept, therefore, is not very helpful in understanding the distribution of Ruff leks. While Bradbury's model is certainly too simple for this species, it does prompt other ideas. Instead of estimating home range sizes, it seems to be more important to discover what the different females are actually doing in the lekking areas. Do they forage? Do they copulate? Do they nest? Or do they join other females or males to migrate further north? Females certainly forage in the lekking areas. Clusters of leks are often very close to suitable feeding grounds (see Section 2.1) which are often visited by large groups of females when feeding conditions are good. For instance, the largest numbers of females were present in Roderwolde when the polder was drained by pumping out the canal water.

Copulating females

To estimate the total number of females copulating on a lek near Roderwolde I want to play with a few data and some additional assumptions. In 1969 I recorded 100 copulations on lek B in Roderwolde. Most activity occurred in the early-morning hours and for that reason the data on early-morning copulations were treated separately from those of the rest of the day. Forty-five copulations were performed before 9.00 a.m., and 55 after 9.00 a.m. I made observations during about three sevenths of the early morning hours of that season, and for about one fifth of the remaining parts of the day. Thus, the total copulation score may be estimated at $(7 \times 45)/3 + (5 \times 55) - 380$. This does not imply that 380 different females copulated on this lek. Females may copulate several times during the same visit. They may also repeatedly visit the same lek for copulation. The average number of copulations per female per visit, during which she performs at least one, is at most two. The average number of visits to the lek per female on which she copulates is certainly small, at most three, because most recognizable females are seen only once, or a few times. Thus, I presume that females copulate on average at most six times on the same lek. This low copulation rate is in accordance with the figures compiled by Birkhead *et al.* for polygynous and promiscuous bird species. It further implies that at least 380/6 = 63 females were inseminated on that lek. In 1969, lek B consisted of, on average, 10 males, all classes lumped together. Thus, per male, more than six females were inseminated. Although females may copulate on different leks, this high number of inseminated females suggests that the sex ratio is strongly skewed towards females.

Breeding females

The number of nesting females in Roderwolde seems to be much lower than the number of inseminated females, presumed on the basis of the assumptions above. Although I searched through the whole study area, covering about 4 km^2, I found only five females who seemed to have a nest or young. I estimate that at most 20 females were breeding in the 25-km^2 area around the cluster of leks near Roderwolde, which consisted of at least 25 males. This indicates that, at the time of breeding, the sex ratio is skewed towards males.

The large discrepancy between the estimated number of inseminated females and the observed number of breeding females might be caused by:

— a very high frequency of nesting failures in early spring; or
— the departure of inseminated females to other breeding areas.

The first possibility cannot be entirely excluded, considering the marginal distribution of the Dutch population, and the rapid changes in agricultural methods during the last few decades. Nevertheless, the majority of females have left the area by the time of breeding and it is unlikely that they have returned to the resting areas for moulting, far less to their winter quarters. Thus, it seems that the second possibility holds. This is also compatible with the observed sex-ratios on the different breeding grounds. The low proportion of breeding females in the Netherlands is compensated for by the high proportion in Finland and the northwestern part of Russia (see Section 4.1).

Storage of sperm

If the females who copulate on southern leks really go to northern breeding grounds to nest, one may question whether they are able to produce fertilized eggs in these areas without copulating again after reaching their final destination. In most birds ovulation and fertilization occur about 24 hours before the egg is laid. Thus, to answer the last question, the interval between copulation on southern leks and laying on the northern breeding grounds must be compared with migration speed, and with the length of the period that viable sperm can be

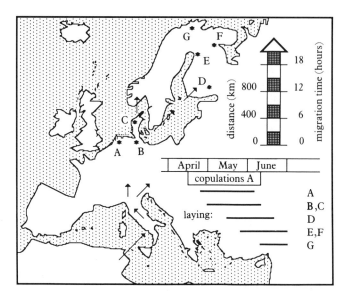

FIGURE 35 *The copulation season in the Netherlands (A), and laying periods in various places in northwestern Europe (A–G).*

stored by the female. Copulation in the Netherlands occurs from 20 April up to 10 June (Figure 35A). Egg-laying starts at the end of April and may continue up to the beginning of June. In Schleswig-Holstein (B) and Denmark (C), the laying period starts and ends about one week later. In southern Finland (D), egg-laying occurs from the middle of May up to the middle of June. In northern Finland (E) and the White Sea region (F) in the Soviet Union, laying starts at the end of May and continues up to the end of June, and, finally, in northeastern Norway (G), laying occurs in the last three weeks of June. Thus, in Europe the interval between the first copulations in the Netherlands and the start of egg-laying on the breeding grounds in the north is at most seven weeks. The interval between the major peak of copulation in the south and the start of laying in the north is about two weeks shorter, whereas the last copulations in the south coincide with the start of laying in the far north of Europe.

The distance between the Dutch leks and the breeding grounds in northern Europe is at most 3000 km. This distance may be traversed in less than two days (see Sections 4.4 and 4.5). However, a heavy female would thereby lose about 40 g of fat, altogether two thirds of her reserves. To be able to produce a full clutch of eggs, the female first has to replenish these reserves, which takes at least eight days (see Section 4.5). Thus, the interval between copulation in the Netherlands and the start of egg-laying on the most northern breeding grounds in Europe would need to be about 10 days.

It is not very likely that females first traverse the whole distance to the north, and then replenish their reserves. At the time of arrival on the northern breeding grounds, food abundance is not at its maximum, and thus the time needed for fattening would exceed eight days. It would therefore pay a female to arrive with her full reserves. Moreover, in view of the short northern season and the timing of the main peak of food availability for young (see Section 4.2), it would also pay her to start egg-laying as early as possible. Females should therefore travel to the northern breeding grounds in a series of short flights between suitable foraging areas, building up as many reserves as possible on the way.

Nothing is known about how long a reeve can go between insemination and the laying of fertile eggs. The fertility of sperm is maintained for at least seven days in all species of birds which have been studied. Almost all the eggs of the domestic chicken are fertilized, provided they are laid within 12 days after copulation. In the domestic turkey, fertilization generally occurs if the eggs are laid within 28 days after copulation. This ability derives from specialized sperm-storage glands in the uterovaginal region of the oviduct. Females of polygynous and promiscuous species seem to have better capacities for sperm storage than their monogamous relatives. Yet a few monogamous species also have remarkable abilities to store viable sperm. The Fulmar, studied by Scott Hatch, seems to be able to store sperm for up to eight weeks. Pair-members of this species meet each other in early spring at the nest site. They court and copulate, and separately return to the ocean to build up reserves for egg-laying and incubation. After three weeks, on average, the female returns to the nest and starts to lay within 24 hours, irrespective of whether she has already met her mate again. Hatch was able to show that sperm were present in the sperm-storage glands of all females collected in May. Sperm-storage glands were also found in Leach's Storm-petrel and in the Horned Puffin. The presence of such glands in the latter species is highly interesting, because the Horned Puffin is distantly related to the Ruff, both species being in the same order (Charadriiformes). In view of these examples, it is certainly possible that reeves also possess sperm storage glands and that they are able to lay fertile eggs two or three weeks after their last copulation. This period would be sufficient to allow for the journey from the Dutch leks to the breeding grounds in northern Europe.

Geographical distribution of males

I now want to consider the possible evolution of a system in which inseminations occurring in southern areas are really important for the fertilization of eggs laid on northern breeding grounds. Such a system might have evolved because it is advantageous to females. A possible benefit would be that females do not waste time in mate selection and mating once they arrive on their breeding grounds. Alternatively, the system might have evolved because it is advantageous to males. Males might profit by the system if the northern breeding grounds were unsuitable for sustaining birds with the characteristics of male Ruffs. This appears unrealistic at first, because reeves survive well in these regions. However, males are much larger than females and need more food. It is significant that those males which do reach the northern breeding grounds usually return south as soon as the mating season is over. Hence, the different geographical preferences of males and females may arise from a mating system which involves strong inter-male competition, and thus selects for large males. The northern breeding grounds provide sub-optimal feeding for larger males which tend not to migrate so far north. This idea is supported by the finding that males from northern Europe have smaller body measurements than those from central Europe (see Section 4.1).

A geographical separation between copulation and breeding would lead to a strong selective pressure on males to stay at places where there is a high probability of intercepting receptive females. Consequently, competition between males for space on the leks would be high in the temperate resting areas. Males with the best competitive abilities, especially the largest independent males, should therefore stay on the southern leks. The smaller independent males would be forced to establish leks on the less favourable sites, further to the north. One might imagine that under such circumstances certain males do not participate in inter-male competition, but specialize in other reproductive strategies, for instance in looking for receptive females. This seems to be a possible route for the evolution of the satellite strategy. Such a strategy would be most useful in areas with low breeding densities, and without any substantial migratory activity, such as many northern breeding grounds. If this idea is correct, one should expect high frequencies of satellites in northern breeding areas and lower frequencies on the southern leks. Earlier discussion (Section 2.5) showed that there are some indications of such a trend.

Summary

The number of females copulating on Dutch leks seems to be much higher than the number of males on those leks. The number of nesting females in these areas, however, is lower than the number of males on leks. This phenomenon is apparently the result of the departure of inseminated females to northern breeding areas. It seems possible that these inseminations lead to the laying of fertilized eggs in harsh breeding habitats far away. This presumed spatial separation between insemination and egg-laying might be an essential factor in the evolution of the two behavioural types found among the males of this species.

CHAPTER 5

Comparison and evolution

After reading the preceding chapters, one may rightly conclude that the Ruff is a most remarkable bird. Its lekking system is extremely complex. Genetic differences between individuals seem to produce a variety of satellite and independent strategies in the males, and sexual dimorphism, both in size and plumage, is strongly developed. Its moulting patterns are complex, especially in the males, whose plumage diversity is extraordinary. Its migratory behaviour is also striking, especially in the differences between males and females. It is difficult not to wonder how this peculiar combination of traits has evolved.

Since Charles Darwin, comparison has been the main basis for tracing the evolutionary roots of a particular taxonomic group or trait. Phylogenetic relationships between species or higher taxa might be revealed by comparing all their properties. The origin of certain traits, such as the behavioural characteristics of a species, may be studied on the basis of detailed comparisons of such traits between various species, whose phylogenetic relationships have been independently established. In the following sections I want to make both types of comparison, initially without trying to discover the evolution of the Ruff's characteristics. That question will be postponed to the end. First I merely want to emphasize the Ruff's taxonomic position, and to describe the variation among the species related to it.

The Ruff has been classified by Jehl in the subfamily Calidridinae, consisting of 23 other sandpiper species, such as the Knot, Sanderling, Western Sandpiper, Little Stint, Pectoral Sandpiper, Purple Sandpiper, Dunlin, and Buff-breasted Sandpiper. According to Strauch, three members of this subfamily deviate in morphology: the Broad-billed Sandpiper, Sanderling, and Buff-breasted Sandpiper. Male Ruffs are among the largest representatives of the subfamily. All these species breed in the boreal, sub-arctic and arctic regions and their main breeding range lies north of the 15°C July isotherm. Most species have their winter quarters in other areas and many are long-distance migrants. Together with five other sub-families, Gallinagininae (snipes), Scolopacinae (woodcocks), Tringinae (godwits, curlews, redshanks, etc.), Arenariinae (turnstones), and Phalaropodinae, they form the family Scolopacidae. According to Strauch, one genus of the Tringinae, *Actitis* (Common and Spotted Sandpiper) has almost identical morphological characteristics to the Calidridinae. Just as in the Calidridinae, almost all representatives of the rest of the family breed in the temperate and cold areas of the northern hemisphere.

There is much debate about the further classification of the group. Joel Cracraft considered this family as the only representative of a superfamily Scolopacoidea (Table 23), which formed the suborder Scolopaci, together with the Jacanoidea (jacanas and painted snipes) which live mainly in the tropics. Other taxonomists, especially Strauch, also include the Thinocoridae (seedsnipes) in the same phylogenetic line. Together with the Alcae (auks) and the Charadriomorpha (crabplovers, gulls, sheathbills, stone curlews, and plovers), this suborder was classified in the order Charadriiformes. Finally, Cracraft considered this order to be related to the Gruiformes (cranes and rails), and the Columbiformes (pigeons): division 5 of the subclass of Neornithes (modern birds).

Early remains

The history of the Charadriiformes can be traced back to the Upper Cretaceous, about 80 million years ago. Pierce Brodkorb listed 73 fossils of paleo-species of this order, seven of which were found in the Upper Cretaceous. Four were classified in an extinct family, the Cimolopterygidae, and three in the Palaeotringinae, an extinct subfamily of the Scolopacidae. A summary of the Scolopacidae fossil record, presented in Figure 36, shows that the Calidridinae were found from the Lower Miocene onwards, over 20 million years ago. A close

Table 23 The phylogenetic classification of recent Charadriiformes (after Cracraft).

Suborder Alcae	
Family Alcidae	Auks
Suborder Charadriomorpha	
Infraorder Dromae	
Family Dromadidae	Crabplovers
Infraorder Lari	
Superfamily Stercorarioidea	
Family Stercorariidae	Skuas
Superfamily Laroidea	
Family Rhynchopidae	Skimmers
Family Laridae	Gulls
Infraorder Chionae	
Family Chionididae	Sheathbills
Family Thinocoridae	Seedsnipes
Infraorder Burhirni	
Family Burhinidae	Thick-knees
Infraorder Charadrii	
Superfamily Haematopodoidea	
Family Haematopodidae	Oystercatchers
Family Recurvirostridae	Avocets
Superfamily Charadrioidea	
Family Glareolidae	Pratincoles
Family Vanellidae	Lapwings
Family Charadriidae	Plovers
Suborder Scolopaci	
Superfamily Jacanoidea	
Family Jacanidae	Jacanas
Family Rostratulidae	Painted snipes
Superfamily Scolopacoidea	
Family Scolopacidae	Sandpipers
Subfamily Calidridinae	Arctic sandpipers
Subfamily Gallinagininae	Snipes and dowitchers
Subfamily Scolopacinae	Woodcocks
Subfamily Tringinae	Godwits and curlews
Subfamily Arenariinae	Turnstones
Subfamily Phalaropodinae	Phalaropes

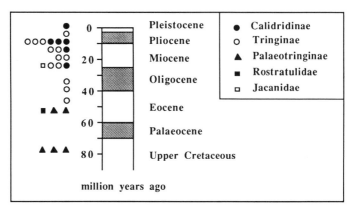

FIGURE 36 *The fossils of the suborder Scolopaci and their dating (after Brod-korb, 1967).*

relative of the Ruff, *Philomachus binagadensis*, was found in the Soviet republic Azerbaidzhan, west of the Caspian Sea, and was dated to the Lower Pleistocene. Modern Ruffs are also known from the Pleistocene and have been found in Denmark, Finland, Czechoslovakia, Hungary, and the Soviet Union (Azerbaidzhan).

Most fossils of the order Charadriiformes were from the Miocene (23 specimens) and Pliocene (16 specimens). Most of these belonged to the subfamily Tringinae (11) of the family Scolopacidae, suborder Scolopaci, to the suborder Alcae (10), and to the infraorder Lari (7) of the suborder Charadriomorpha. All three suborders were represented from the Eocene onwards, about 60 million years ago. This points to a very early evolution of this order as compared with the remains of Archaeopteryx, from about 140 million years ago. In fact several well-defined genus types, such as *Limosa* (godwits) and *Tringa* (redshanks, etc.) date back to the Eocene. The neo-species, however, evolved much later and no clear examples of such species have been reported from before the Pleistocene.

The climate as an evolutionary force

Many, in fact the large majority, of the representatives of the three suborders of the Charadriiformes breed in the northern hemisphere, especially in the boreal, sub-arctic, and arctic regions, in or close to the circumpolar tundra habitats. This breeding distribution is most clearly displayed by the Calidridinae. It has been stressed by Sten Larson that the breeding distribution of almost every species of bird is restricted to a particular climatic regime: cold, temperate or warm. This phenomenon, which is also displayed by several higher taxa, was described as

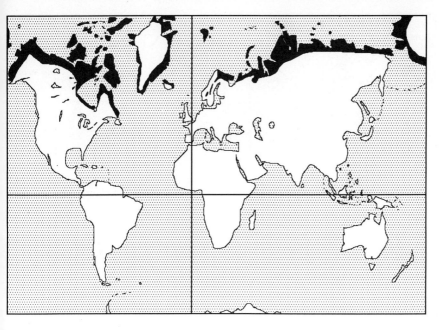

<small>FIGURE</small> 37 *The recent distribution of tundra vegetation.*

the *ecoclimatic rule*. He assumed that this rule also holds for species living in the past, and that, in general, modern species living in a particular climatic area were descended from ancestors who lived under similar circumstances. By applying these principles Larson tried to explain the phylogeny of the order Charadriiformes. In view of the recent breeding distributions, one would expect that the common ancestors of this taxon, especially those of the Calidridinae, had a cold breeding habitat. However, during the main part of the Tertiary, when the different genera evolved, the climate was much warmer, especially in Eurasia and North America. Although the temperature gradually decreased during this period, the first glaciations in Iceland, Greenland, and in the Sierra Nevada in North America did not appear until the Pliocene, about three million years ago. At that time the distribution of the tundra habitat was probably similar to its range now (Figure 37).

Thus, according to Larson, in the course of the evolution of this order, there must have been a gradual adaptation to temperate and cold breeding habitats. The first forms, which adapted to breeding in temperate habitats, probably left the warm subtropical lowlands and became established in the highlands of Greenland, the Rocky Mountains and the Sierra Nevada in western North America, and the Himalayas in central Asia. Later forms which invaded the temperate areas probably pushed the earlier colonists out to colder areas,

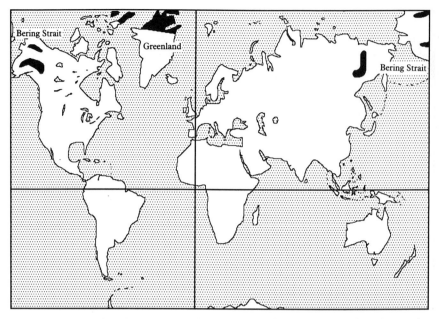

FIGURE 38 *The distribution of tundra vegetation during the interglacial periods.*

because they were in the best position to evolve adaptations for more extreme conditions. Such selection pressure due to new invasions of other forms might have been the cause of all recent representatives of the Calidridinae breeding under much more extreme conditions than their common ancestors during the Miocene or even earlier.

The genesis of new species occurred mainly during these Tertiary epochs. Larson pointed out that there must have been several waves of invasion in the temperate and cold regions. Quite often, after adaptation to these colder habitats, the populations from Eurasia and North America became geographically isolated. This could have led to the formation of species-pairs, such as the Knot (North America) and the Great Knot (Eurasia) which probably formed during the late Pliocene. Pairs, such as the Buff-breasted Sandpiper (North America) and the Ruff (Eurasia), are probably from an earlier date, perhaps early Pliocene (see Figure 40).

During the Pleistocene four successive glacial periods were associated with considerable fluctuations in the climate. The interglacial periods were marked by a minimal distribution of tundra habitats, restricted to northern Greenland and the highlands on either side of the Bering Strait (Figure 38). The glacial periods were marked by very large tundra areas. For instance, during the latest

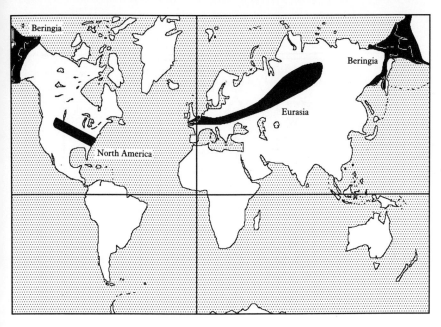

FigURE 39 *The distribution of tundra vegetation during the last glaciation.*

glaciation an enormous tundra area extended from France up to central Siberia; a second considerable area, Beringia, bridged eastern Siberia and Alaska, which were connected with each other during this period; and a third, somewhat smaller, tundra area was situated in central North America, south of the Great Lakes (Figure 39). In spite of these fluctuations in the climate, and the associated growth and decline of the tundra areas, judging by the fossil record only a few new lineages evolved during the Pleistocene. Within the subfamily Calidridinae, probably four species-pairs were formed by the splitting up of ancestral pre-glacial species. A clear example is the Little Stint, which probably stayed in Greenland during the interglacial periods and in Eurasia during the last glaciation, and the Red-necked Stint, which probably stayed in Beringia during the interglacial periods and during the last glaciation (see Figure 40). The cyclic appearance, growth and shrinking of the tundra habitats must also have played a very important role in determining the present distribution of the various species.

Using Larson's work and other relevant literature, I have tried to reconstruct the phylogeny of the Calidridinae, starting from the assumption that there was only one common ancestor. Figure 40 shows the result of my efforts. At the left side, besides the species names, are shown the breeding distributions during the latest glaciation and thereafter. To the right, the most probable breeding

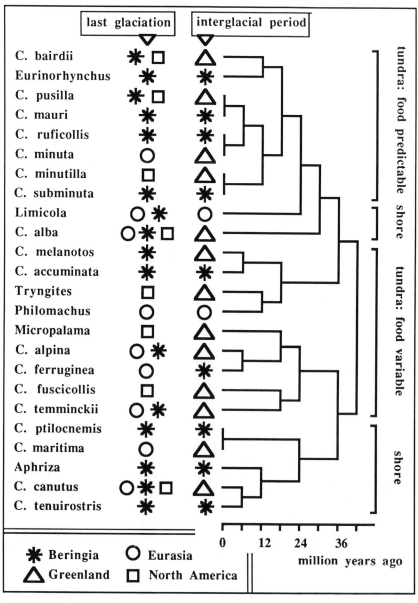

FIGURE 40 *The possible lineage for calidridine sandpipers.*

distributions during the interglacial periods are given. The resulting pattern of branching shows one of the most probable phylogenetic trees. At each split of two branches, one (the higher) represents the North American component, and the other (the lower) the Eurasian component. The terminal patterns of splitting between species are fairly certain, dating included. The pattern of branching becomes more and more uncertain the higher the level of branching, though the dating of the different branches, relative to one other, seems to be a reasonable approximation. Dating on a geological time scale, however, is only a guess. There are four main branches in this scheme. The upper one includes species which are mainly adapted to breed in tundra areas with a low but fairly predictable food supply, and also two species of the seashores. The second and third branch include the species of tundra areas with an unpredictable, but in some years extensive, food supply, and the fourth branch includes shoreline species. The position of the Ruff is in agreement with the suggestions made by Pitelka *et al*.

Because of highly differing conditions in the course of their genesis, it cannot be excluded that many of the recent taxonomic groups within the Charadrii-formes are derived from more than one ancestor. In other words, the taxonomic categories do not clearly reflect phylogenetic relationships. There are several indications of this. First, the considerable disagreement among taxonomists about the classification of the Charadriiformes suggests that phylogenetic relationships are only poorly revealed. Second, more specifically, an analysis by Mickevich and Parenti revealed that certain genera, for instance Calidris, have probably evolved from more than one phylogenetic lineage. Third, it is some-what improbable that, during the relatively warm Tertiary epochs, all represen-tatives of a certain taxon, for instance the Calidridinae, adapted to the same climatic conditions of extreme cold.

Non-climatic factors

Adaptation to extreme climatic conditions in the past may have played a major role in the evolution of the Charadriiformes. However, it is possible that certain other characteristics of the ancestor species pre-adapted them for breeding in a tundra habitat. One of the most striking features of this ecotype is the enormous seasonal change of temperature and snow cover, rendering food unavailable during the winter, and forcing the birds which exploit it to migrate elsewhere. Therefore, it is likely that the ancestors of these birds also had migratory habits, possibly to exploit areas with strongly fluctuating food supplies. This can be exemplified by another feature of the tundra: the sudden emergence of adult diptera (see Section 4.2 and Figure 31). Tundra birds are highly dependent on this resource, timing their eggs to hatch when adult diptera become available so that their young can feed mainly on them during their first weeks of life. Such short peaks in the availability of prey types may also occur in other habitats, for example the inundation zones near rivers after heavy rainfall, and moors after very wet periods. One might surmise that the ancestors of the Calidridinae evolved in such habitats and exploited the peaks in availability of prey for their young. This idea is supported by the fact that almost all recent representatives of the Calidridinae possess adaptations which are extremely helpful for life in such wet or marshy habitats. They have relatively long legs, suitable for wading, and relatively long bills, suitable for catching small prey by stitching and probing in the mud (see Section 4.2). Their bills are highly adapted for such foraging by virtue of the many tactile sense cells, the so-called Herbst corpuscles, present in the bony bill tip.

Summary

The Ruff has been classified in the hierarchy: subfamily Calidridinae (arctic sandpipers), family Scolopacidae (sandpipers and allies), order Charadrii-formes. All its close relatives breed in the temperate and cold regions of the northern hemisphere. Most of them overwinter in temperate and tropical regions, and thus are long-distance migrants. The fossil record of this group extends over the last 80 million years. The first discovered Calidridinae lived over 20 million years ago. The evolution of this group is considered to be strongly influenced by the climate, which was much warmer during most of that time. The group's ancestors probably lived in the colder mountain areas. The formation of the modern species seems to be due to fluctuations in the climate and in the extent of suitable habitat during the Pleistocene, which experienced four successive glacial periods. Evolution in this group also seems to have been influenced by the ability to migrate and to utilize short peaks in prey availability in wet and marshy habitats.

5.2 COURTSHIP AND MATING PATTERN

Ruffs differ in many respects from most of their close relatives. A review of the variety of social systems within the order Charadriiformes is given in Table 24. In most of these relatives the males and females establish monogamous pair-bonds, and usually exhibit biparental care of the offspring. In many of these species the male performs most care after the eggs hatch; in some species from the start of incubation onwards. In a few relatives sex-roles are completely reversed. In a few others the female typically produces two clutches of eggs, of which the first is incubated and cared for by the male, and the second by the female (double clutching). In several species related to the Ruff the social relationships between males and females are even more complex. Polyandrous relationships, in which one female pairs with more than one male, are fairly common, especially among species with sex-role reversal. Polygynous relation-

Table 24 Social organization in recent Charadriiformes.

Family	species (no.)	mon	dcl	srr	pan	pgy	pmc	lek
Alcidae	22	us						
Dromadidae	1	pr						
Stercorariidae	4	us						
Rhynchopidae	3	us						
Laridae	82	us				oc	oc	
Chionididae	2	us						
Thinocoridae	4	pr				pr		
Burhinidae	9	us						
Haematopodidae	6	us						
Recurvirostridae	7	us						
Glareolidae	17	us						
Vanellidae	24	us				oc		
Charadriidae	40	us	≧1	≧2	≧2	oc		
Jacanidae	8	1?		us	us			
Rostratulidae	2	1?		1	1			
Scolopacidae	84	us	≧3	≧4	≧3	±5	±5	≧3
Calidridinae	24	us	≧3	tt	oc	±2	±4	≧2
Gallinagininae	18	us				1?	≧1	≧1
Scolopacinae	6					pr		
Tringinae	31	us		≧1	≧1	oc		
Arenariinae	2	us						
Phalaropodinae	3	us		3	≧2			

Key: mon, monogamy; dcl, double clutching; srr, sex-role reversal; pan, polyandry; pgy, polygyny; pmc, promiscuity; lek, lekking. Numbers refer to number of species which usually display the social organization indicated; us, usual pattern in most species; pr, perhaps a usual pattern in these species; tt, many species tend towards this pattern; oc, occasionally in one or a few species.

ships, in which one male pairs with more than one female, also seem to occur in some species. Promiscuous relationships, in which pair-bonds are essentially absent, have been found in only a few species, among them the Ruff. Here, I want to compare the special features of the Ruff to similar characteristics in other species, both related and non-related.

Promiscuity

In at least three species of the Calidridinae no real pair-bonds are formed. It is self-evident that the Ruff belongs to this group, as do the Pectoral Sandpiper and the Buff-breasted Sandpiper, both described in detail by Myers. The mating pattern of the Sharp-tailed Sandpiper, which is considered to be polygynous, is possibly also better described as being promiscuous. The distinction between polygyny and promiscuity, especially in the Calidridinae, is vague. As in polygynous species, females of promiscuous species perform all the parental care. The use of the male's territory is also restricted to courtship and mating. Territory size varies from rather large, such as in Buff-breasted Sandpipers, to very small, as in the Ruff. The displays of the males are very conspicuous. Whereas visual signals play a major role in the behaviour of Ruffs and Buff-breasted Sandpipers, Pectoral and Sharp-tailed Sandpipers also use sounds, produced during flight by means of a fat-filled breast sac which is pumped up and down. This feathered breast sac strongly recalls the lower part of the nuptial collar of the Ruff. Male Pectoral Sandpipers make deep hooting calls, like the sound of a foghorn; male Sharp-tailed Sandpipers give a dry, crackling warble. Females may visit several males before copulating and males may copulate with several females.

Within the family Scolopacidae promiscuity is known from one other species, the Great Snipe, studied by Lemnell, Avery and Sherwood and more recently by Jacob Höglund. Outside the family, but within the order Charadriiformes, promiscuity is also rare. Solely promiscuous mating systems are unknown in this group but in certain subgroups, especially in colonial seabirds, isolated promiscuous matings may occur though monogamous pair-bonds are typical. In other taxonomic groups also, predominantly promiscuous mating systems are not very common.

Communal display

The males of most, if not all, promiscuous species of the Scolopacidae display communally on leks. This especially holds for the Ruff, the Buff-breasted Sandpiper, and the Great Snipe. Members of the first two species interact on leks during the daylight hours, mainly by visual displays; members of the last species visit their leks at night, using mainly vocal signals. On the leks of all three species, males defend territories which are visited by females. Lekking is unknown in other families of the Charadriiformes, though it is quite common in some other avian groups, such as the grouse, manakins, and birds of paradise.

In many species of animals of highly differing taxonomic groups, males assemble on leks during the reproductive period to court females. Usually these sites are used solely for copulation. Egg-laying and nesting, or parturition, by the female, and foraging by male and female, usually occur elsewhere. In a few species, however, especially fish and frogs, communal display is mainly restricted to the spawning sites and quite often the males use the same area year after year. As well as in birds, communal display occurs in insects such as fireflies, Hawaiian fruitflies, and locusts, in fish such as cichlids and barbels, in amphibians such as frogs, and in mammals such as open-country antelopes and fruit bats. Communal display in animals may be highly spectacular, due to synchronization of visual or vocal signals by a large number of males. Lekking seems to enhance the attractiveness of the males, because females tend to prefer groups of males over single ones. Thus, males seem to be more likely to encounter receptive females when they are in a group than when they display alone.

A number of ecological factors are closely associated with lek behaviour, and probably promoted its evolution. Lekking only occurs in species in which the female performs all the parental duties, and individuals of lekking species usually feed in flocks or herds. Steve Emlen and Lewis Oring predicted that their resources are so distributed in space and time that the needs of a single animal, a monogamous pair, or a polygynous association, cannot adequately be defended, and this case might also hold for the Ruff. The prediction was confirmed by, among others, one of my colleagues, Gerrit de Vos, in a study of Black Grouse. Lekking further occurs in species in which the number of displaying males is higher than the number of receptive females. This factor has also been stressed by Emlen and Oring, a fact which also implies that the resources cannot easily be defended. Receptive females may be considered as a resource for displaying males. Hence, a relatively low number of receptive females implies that only some of the males may have access to these females, which, in turn, promotes inter-male competition for females. The main mechanisms for such competition comprise fighting and other forms of aggression among males, and disruption of the mating attempts of other males.

Satellite strategies

In several species of animals, areas which are defended or claimed by a particular individual may also be utilized by other individuals of the same species. This clearly applies to mates and offspring, but in certain cases also to other conspecifics. One possibility implies that conspecifics may parasitize resources of the territory owner, simply by avoiding the notice or control of the owner. For instance, owners who defend large territories may lose control over one corner when patrolling in another corner. In the meantime intruders can exploit the resources in the undefended corner of the territory. Intruders may also hide, or behave in a way which reduces the probability of their being attacked, for instance by mimicking a receptive female. These so-called *sneaky strategies* are known with respect to the food resources in a territory, but also to mating opportunities. This latter situation is especially important for lekking animals. Earlier in this book I described examples of such a strategy in Red Deer, Field Crickets, Bullfrogs, Three-spined Sticklebacks, Mediterranean *Tripterygion* species, and the Bluegill Sunfish (see Section 2.8). Sneaky strategies may also entail the disruption of a neighbour's mating opportunities. This factor seems to play an important role in mate choice in the Cock-of-the-Rock, studied by Trail. In a few close relatives of the Ruff, too, sexual activity of the

Squatting resident male with satellite (in front), squatting resident male alone on residence (behind), and standing female in between (left) (photo Joop Brink-kemper)

males may be obstructed by aggressive encounters with other males. In Buff-breasted Sandpipers, and probably in Great Snipes, these other males may mimic females to disrupt the interactions between a territorial male and a female. This recalls the satellite strategy in the Ruff, but, whereas territorial behaviour in the Ruff is usually not shown by satellite individuals, territorial behaviour and female mimicking in Buff-breasted Sandpipers and Great Snipes is performed by the same individuals.

Another possible reason for the joint use of a territory by an owner and a subordinate unrelated conspecific is that these subordinates can also bring benefits, e.g. they may help to defend the territory. These *satellite strategies* are also known with respect to food resources in a territory. For instance, Nick Davies and Alasdair Houston observed that Pied Wagtails wintering in England sometimes tolerated a subordinate conspecific on their feeding territory. The food resource consisted of small insects, continuously supplied by a river. The yield was high if the banks of the river were visited after a sufficiently long interval; this could be regulated by making systematic searching rounds through the whole territory. But intruders could disturb this pattern, often causing a considerably lower yield. The wagtails who tolerated satellites, however, were much more successful at keeping intruders out of their territories, and thus at optimally exploiting their food resources. The small, regular loss of food to a satellite was less than that resulting from the constant disruption from numerous intruders. Satellite strategies with respect to mating opportunities are not well known among animals. Besides the Ruff, I have described one example in this book, namely the Waterbuck in Kenya (see p. 95). Also, I have earlier drawn a parallel with the social organization of Chimpanzees and with other variants of 'helping'.

The evolution of sneaky and satellite strategies may, according to Madhav Gadgil, be the result of strong competition among males for access to females or other resources. The main reason for this is that males, who compete for females, may invest considerably before they get any chance at copulation. This would promote the development of non-competitive strategies, which do not need prior investment, but which utilize particular mating opportunities. This might imply that individuals merely make the best of a bad job. They may display sneaky strategies when their competitive abilities are not sufficiently developed and may later switch roles after developing such abilities. Alternatively, it might imply that certain genotypes develop into sneaky or into satellite strategists, and other genotypes into competitive strategists. This would even be possible if mating success per unit time for such non-competitive strategists was much lower than in the competitive strategists. This would follow if competitive strategists do not get mating opportunities before a certain age, and if competition also leads to high mortality rates, so that sneaky strategists can mate at a lower rate for a longer period of time. Thus, high mating success per unit of time does not necessarily imply that competitive strategists perform on average more copulations per lifetime than non-competitive strategists.

Terrestrial display

Ruffs display almost entirely on the ground, in contrast to most related species, except those displaying on leks. Although terrestrial display does occur in these relatives, aerial acrobatics play a major role in their courtship and territorial defence. Only jacanas and painted snipes share this distinction from most other Charadriiformes. In several other groups of birds, terrestrial display is highly developed. This is clearly the case for ratite birds and several species of penguins, which are unable to fly and do not swim during courtship. Terrestrial display also predominates in gallinaceous birds, in cranes and bustards, and in a few passerine families, such as lyrebirds and bowerbirds. Ground display may be very important in colonial seabirds, such as albatrosses, boobies, cormorants, and gulls. In these latter groups, however, aerial display, and sometimes displays on the water, play a supplementary or even a predominant role.

Purely terrestrial display is fairly common in species which do not depend very much on their wings for locomotion. For instance, most gallinaceous birds, lyrebirds, and bowerbirds are non-migratory. Yet purely terrestrial display is not restricted to such groups. For instance, cranes and bustards may fly considerable distances between their winter quarters and breeding grounds but their ground display often includes elaborate and conspicuous movements with the wings, similar to the wing-fluttering, flutter-jumping, and hovering in the Ruff (see Section 2.7 and Figure 19). Thus, here also, wing quality might play a role in mate selection. This may lead to selection for wing quality of the offspring.

Lek B near Roderwolde, 1967. Wing-fluttering, especially by Grandpa on the left.

Purely terrestrial display is rather common among gregarious species, which may also court and mate in groups. Terrestrial display of several birds together is conspicuous, and therefore perhaps attractive for the other sex. Moreover, it may prevent confusion about the *identity* of the participants. This latter feature is extremely important for mate selection. Communal aerial displays are rare, probably because they would create confusion among the members of the other sex. Communal displays on water and in trees do occur, but these also may lead to confusion about identity. Thus, the evolution of terrestrial display in the Ruff seems to be closely related to the evolution of communal display, most probably through the preference of females for identifiable males of proven quality: among its relatives terrestrial display does occur, but there is none on water or in trees.

Silence

In contrast to almost all other species of the Charadriiformes, Ruffs display without making any sound. Their exceptional position in the Calidridinae may be allied to their terrestrial display, since almost all close relatives vocalize during aerial display. Similarly, Buff-breasted Sandpipers, which also display on the ground, are mainly silent. In contrast, the Great Snipe makes a lot of noise. This latter species, however, makes limited use of visual signals, as it displays during the night. In fact, the Ruff's extremely scarce use of sounds is exceptional among birds. Adult Ruffs only vocalize when alarmed and to some extent during nocturnal migration.

The silence of Ruffs on the leks may be linked to two factors. In the first place, it seems important for leks to be *detectable by flying conspecifics*. This factor may be exaggerated, because the Ruff's leks seem to serve a wide area. It is highly probable that visual signals are more effective for this purpose than vocal signals. In the second place, it seems to be important for leks to be *secure against predators*. Visual conspicuousness, however, imposes the cost of being vulnerable to aerial predators. Protection against such predators is afforded by the Ruff's attentiveness to conspecifics passing overhead. I have the strong impression that this protection is rather effective. I frequently saw Ruffs on leks react to aerial predators, either by freezing altogether, or by flying off. Only once did I observe such a predator, a Marsh Harrier, succeed in catching a Ruff, by approaching the lek from behind my observation tent. The scarce use of sounds may serve as a protection against terrestrial predators, such as stoats, foxes, and perhaps lynx, and, of course, also cats in inhabited areas. I believe that these predators may cause severe damage to a lek, when they accidentally detect the site. They may hide in the close vicinity of a lek, choose their moment to pounce, and return later to inflict further damage.

The relationship between vulnerability to predation and conspicuousness of display is well established in several taxa. Most species of birds which display on the ground and combine conspicuous visual signals with conspicuous vocal ones are relatively large, and thus not very vulnerable to predators. For these large species – ratites, bustards, cranes, and grouse – the risk of being taken by a predator is small. For the smaller species, such as quail and hemipodes, the risk is much greater, and it is therefore understandable that most do not behave very conspicuously. They rarely live in open areas, commonly have a simple social organization, such as monogamy with biparental care, and rarely use visual signals, communicating mainly by vocal behaviour. Great Snipes fit reasonably well into this pattern. Although they do stay in fairly open areas and have a complex social system, they display only at night, and do not emphasize visual features, but advertise mainly by vocal signals. Ruffs and Buff-breasted Sandpipers display during the daylight hours. They have to live in open areas, because their breeding habitat leaves them no other option. Both species deviate further from the pattern of inconspicuous species by their complex social organization, and by the importance of visual signals. Yet they do fit into this pattern by restricting the conspicuousness of their display through the omission of vocal signals.

Separation between insemination and fertilization

Among the Ruff's relatives a few species show a tendency for separating copulation and egg-laying. According to Oring, Buff-breasted Sandpipers, besides lekking in the breeding areas, may also form temporary leks during migration. This phenomenon creates the opportunity for insemination during migration, and thus fertilization of later eggs. Baird's Sandpipers, which usually establish monogamous pair-bonds, may also display communally on exposed sites close to their breeding grounds, until these can be occupied following snow melt. This species probably uses its communal courtship areas to find former mates or select new ones, but not to perform promiscuous copulations. It is quite tempting to suggest that, in this species also, females are inseminated before they can settle on the breeding grounds. This would enable the males to spend all their time establishing a feeding territory after snow melt, and the females to start egg-laying as soon as possible.

In several groups of animals, insemination of females by males is clearly separated from fertilization of the eggs. The queen in a honeybee colony is able to lay fertilized eggs for years after a few inseminations obtained during one nuptial flight. She stores the sperm and fertilizes the eggs, one after another, just before laying. Females of many other species of insects also produce fertilized eggs for long periods after one or a few inseminations. They have a remarkable ability to store viable sperm for months or even for years. In the internally fertilizing vertebrates this ability is less well developed. In most mammalian species insemination has to take place during the female's fertile period to ensure successful fertilization. In most species of birds, copulations are also common at the time of ovulation, about 24 hours before laying the egg. In several monogamous species copulations may occur from an early stage of pair-formation onwards, sometimes several weeks or even months before egg-laying. Since these early copulations may occur before the testes are fully developed, it is unlikely that they all achieve insemination. Yet there may be a considerable interval between insemination and fertilization of the eggs in some species of birds. For instance, female Black Grouse may lay up to 16 eggs after just one copulation on a lek. In Section 4.6 I gave more examples of such long intervals in birds. In reptiles the intervals between insemination and fertilization may be still longer, sometimes several months or even years. The female may thus utilize the best conditions for each of two different activities: mate selection and egg-laying.

In the internally fertilizing species, the male parent is not necessarily present at the time of egg-laying or parturition. If there is no real bond between male and female, the longer the interval between insemination by the male and egg-laying or parturition by the female, the lower is the probability that the male will be present at that time. Thus, the shortness of this interval may reflect the capability of the species for developing parental care by the male. This interval duration depends on two factors. The initial part of the interval comprises the duration of sperm storage, the time between insemination and fertilization, which is usually short in mammals, short to fairly long in birds, and rather long to very long in reptiles. The final part of the interval comprises the duration of egg-development from fertilization to parturition, which is usually very long in mammals, short in birds, and short to relatively long in reptiles. Thus, in birds, the opportunity to develop male parental care is associated mainly with variation in the duration of sperm storage. This seems to correspond with the few data available. In most species able to store sperm for considerable periods, females are able to perform all the parental duties. By contrast, the females of most species with biparental care, or with male parental care, do not store sperm for long periods. The case of the Ruff seems to be consistent with these trends. The parental abilities of reeves do not require parental aid by the males, and thus do not restrict the potential for storing sperm. Nevertheless, there are exceptions to these trends. For instance, in the Fulmar (see Section 4.6) both parents care for the offspring, but sperm may be stored for rather long periods. Such exceptions, however, are also marked by a very strong monogamous relationship between the parents, which enables the male parent to be present at the time of parturition (egg-laying) or shortly thereafter.

Summary

In contrast to the other members of the Charadriiformes, except Buff-breasted Sandpipers and Great Snipes, Ruffs mate promiscuously on leks. In all species this characteristic is combined with strong inter-male competition for mates, the absence of feeding territories, and parental care by the female only. Regarding species related to the Ruff, there are hardly any data which hint at alternative mating strategies among males. The closest resemblance occurs in the other two lekking species, in which males may mimic females and obtain extra copulations by this behaviour. Sneaky and satellite strategies seem to be the result of strong competition among males for access to females. The Ruff displays almost entirely while standing or sitting on the ground, in contrast to most relatives, which perform elaborate aerial displays. Terrestrial display is considered to be an adaptation in gregarious species to prevent confusion about the identity of the participants. Ruffs utter almost no sounds during their display, whereas vocalizations play an important role in territorial and courtship displays of all related species except Buff-breasted Sandpipers. Lack of vocalization in Ruffs may be seen as an adaptation for protection against predators. Finally, female Ruffs might be distinct from female relatives in the ability to separate, both temporally and spatially, insemination from fertilization and development of eggs. Long intervals between insemination and fertilization are most often associated with no parental care or parental care by the female only. It is remarkable that most of these different aspects of courtship and mating pattern in the Ruff also occur in the other two related species displaying on leks, but not in most other non-lekking relatives.

5.3 VARIATION IN SIZE AND PLUMAGE

In most species of polygynous, promiscuous, and lekking birds the sexes are highly dissimilar. Most commonly the males are brighter and larger than the females. This pattern also applies to the Ruff, but not to most other species of waders, including those displaying on leks, such as Buff-breasted Sandpipers and Great Snipes. In the Ruff, conspicuous morphological variation is not restricted to sexual dimorphism. Inter-individual variation of plumage in male Ruffs is remarkable and seems to be much better developed than in any other species. In this chapter I want to discuss these aspects of intra-specific variation in the Ruff.

Sexual dimorphism

Sexual dimorphism in physical characteristics, body size included, may evolve because of preferences displayed by females for particular features in males, supplemented by natural selection on females for optimal functioning in a particular environment. Thus, the physical differences between males and females of promiscuous and polygynous species may concern body structures used by males for attracting females. For instance, male fruit bats have large muzzles and larynxes for use as a vocal instrument during display, male Sage Grouse possess a chest sac for a similar purpose, and male Ruffs have colourful plumage used as a visual signal during display. In most of the Ruff's close relatives, plumage differences between males and females are absent; in the remaining few, for instance the polygynous Curlew Sandpiper, inter-sexual differences are much smaller than in the Ruff.

The evolution of large males in polygynous and promiscuous mating systems seems to be related to the importance of *body-power*, or fighting, in the competition between males. Large body size would increase the probability of winning contests with other males, and thus increase copulation frequency. For instance, male size in Black Grouse is associated with the ability to defend a mating territory at the best site, male size in Red Deer may be related to battles among males for the control of a harem, and male size in the Northern Elephant Seal (*Mirounga angustirostris*) may be related to rank in the social hierarchy. The importance of body-power in the evolution of large males is supported by other physical characteristics, such as the ownership of weaponry or defensive structures in males. For instance, cocks possess spurs, Red Deer stags have antlers, and Northern Elephant Seal bulls have very thick skins. Sexual dimorphism in promiscuous species does not necessarily imply that males are larger than females. In several species of hummingbirds and manakins, plumage dimorphism between males and females is not combined with sexual size dimorphism. In a few species of the same groups, plumage diversity between the sexes is even combined with reversed sexual size dimorphism (small males and larger females).

The data on sexual size dimorphism in the Ruff are in accordance with the idea that fighting is important. Size dimorphism is most pronounced between females and independent males. For the latter, body-power certainly plays an important role in attaining social status. Size dimorphism is somewhat less between females and satellites, the latter depending less than independent males on body-power for successful copulations. Male Ruffs, however, do not seem to possess specific organs or structures which enable them to attack more efficiently than females, or to protect themselves against attacks. In two promiscuous relatives, Pectoral and Sharp-tailed Sandpipers, males are also larger than females, but the difference is less extreme than in the Ruff. The lack of clear sexual size dimorphism in Buff-breasted Sandpipers and Great Snipes does not agree with the idea that body-power is important, because males of both species do fight amongst one another. Sexual dimorphism in these species might be absent because males are able to increase copulation frequencies by mimicking females. In some animal species, especially fish, one and the same individual may combine sexual dimorphism with female mimicry by the ability to rapidly change patterns and colours. Birds and mammals lack this ability, so in species which benefit from female mimicry the evolution of sexual dimorphism is not very likely. In Ruffs, independent males clearly display their sex, but satellites and naked-nape males seem to mimic the behaviour of females (see Section 2.8).

Size dimorphism in most other waders

In contrast to the Ruff, many representatives of the Charadriiformes, especially the Scolopacidae, have slightly smaller males than females. This so-called 'reversed sexual size dimorphism' has puzzled several investigators. Reversed sexual size dimorphism is most extreme in polyandrous species. By analogy with normal sexual size dimorphism, strong inter-female competition for territories or for mates might be the most important selective force in polyandrous species. Less extreme reversed sexual size dimorphism is also common among the monogamous representatives of the Scolopacidae. Several hypotheses, including differential niche utilization between males and females, have been proposed to explain this phenomenon, although few of these explanations can be supported by satisfactory evidence.

   Jehl and Murray demonstrated rather convincingly that reversed sexual size dimorphism is usually shown by species in which males perform elaborate aerial displays during the period of pair-formation, but rarely by species in which males perform simple aerial displays or courtship on the ground. These latter species usually show normal sexual size dimorphism, though the differences between the sexes are only slight. These observations strongly suggest that reversed sexual size dimorphism is mainly due to a preference of females for males highly agile in aerial display. Since flight ability is extremely important for long-distance migrants, such as most waders (but not necessarily male Ruffs), this kind of female preference is also relevant from a biological point of view.

   A few years ago I suggested, as an alternative or additional hypothesis, that reversed sexual size dimorphism was a consequence of role differentiation between males and females. My main argument for this was that reversed sexual size dimorphism is associated with sex-role reversal, or with breeding systems, characteristic of many waders, in which the male performs most parental care. Female waders seem to be specialized for laying a number of large eggs which develop into highly precocial young. Indeed, complete clutches of eggs in charadriiform birds may comprise more than 50% of the female's body weight, requiring a considerable investment of body reserves. In view of the short arctic summer, natural selection should favour large females, which are able to lay such a clutch within a very short period. The males of these species seem to be specialized for incubating. In view of the low arctic temperatures, they should be adapted for spending the maximum time on the nest, and should leave it as little as possible for foraging. Thus, natural selection should favour small males, who are able to survive and to incubate a full clutch with little food.

Inter-individual variation

Variation in visual characteristics between male Ruffs is extreme in comparison with other species, and individuals can easily be recognized by an observer without colour-ringing the birds. In only a few other species is variation in appearance large enough to permit such individual recognition. For instance, individual Bewick's Swans, studied by Dafila Scott, could be recognized by natural variation in bill pattern. To what extent, however, the animals themselves use such variation for individual recognition is largely unknown. Much more is known about the role of sounds in this regard. The main reason for this is that sounds can easily be separated from the other characteristics of an individual, and can be taped and played back in an experimental situation. In this way several species of songbirds and gulls have been shown to react differently to sounds of territorial neighbours and non-neighbours, or to sounds of mates and non-mates. Thus, there is very strong evidence that birds may use sound to identify individual conspecifics. It is plausible, therefore, that the territorial songs in most species of the Calidridinae are also used for the identification of individuals.

There is at least one remarkable study in which the use of visual characters for identification of individuals has been clearly demonstrated. Philip Whitfield observed marked plumage variability in Turnstones. Black markings on the head, back, and belly differ both in size and in shape between individuals. To test whether these birds were able to recognize a neighbour purely on the basis of these markings, Whitfield made glass fibre dummies, painted to reproduce exactly the same patterns as the real birds in his population. Then he caught a few territorial males and replaced them by such dummies resembling either that particular individual or other males in the population. Neighbours of these experimental territories reacted quite differently to both types of dummies. Dummies resembling the territorial owner were rarely approached very closely, and almost never attacked. Dummies resembling other males, however, were often approached and frequently attacked by their neighbours. Thus, variation in visual characteristics in the Turnstone is certainly important for the individual recognition of conspecifics. This probably holds also for the Ruff in view of its enormous variation in visual features. The evolution of visual rather than vocal cues for identification in this species probably relates closely to the evolution of visual display.

If plumage diversity in the Ruff really serves individual recognition, one might question which relationships between individuals need verification of identity. Is it important for resident males to recognize their neighbours, their satellites, and the visitors at the border of the lek? Is it important for satellites to recognize their hosts, other individual satellites, and individual marginal males? Is it important for females to recognize individual males? Several of these possibilities might be confirmed. For instance, recognition of individual males by a female is important because she may visit the lek several times before copulating.

It is also important for resident males to recognize neighbours, because boundaries and other arrangements are established between individuals. New neighbours may violate these rules, and thus have to be attacked to re-establish the status quo. I have some indirect evidence that resident males indeed use plumage characteristics for identification of neighbours. I observed at least five cases in which a new resident male established himself on a lek by replacing another possessing almost precisely the same plumage characteristics. It even seemed that these intruding males actively selected males resembling themselves when conquering their residences. None of these intruding males had serious problems with his neighbours, whereas other new males were usually fiercely attacked by their neighbours.

The mutual relationship between resident male and satellite also requires individual recognition, especially recognition of the host by the satellite. Recognition of the satellite is less important than recognition of the host, since the host gains direct advantages from satellite visits (attraction of more females), irrespective of the individual who plays the role of satellite (see Section 2.6 and Table 17). In contrast, the benefits to the satellite (copulations) may only be realized after a considerable time, most often after several visits to the same resident male (see Section 2.7).

In view of this, one might expect that selection pressures for characters able to identify individuals are the strongest for independent males. Satellite males would mainly be subject to selection pressures for being identifiable as a class. These hypotheses are supported by the following data: plumage variety among independent males is extremely large, whereas plumage diversity among satellites is much smaller (see Section 2.5 and Table 11).

Summary

The evolution of sexual dimorphism in the plumage of the Ruff seems to be the result of preferences displayed by females for mating partners. The evolution of sexual size dimorphism in the Ruff is probably due to the importance of aggressive competition in males. In most other species of waders sexual size dimorphism is reversed. This might be explained by a preference of females for highly agile males in aerial display. In the Ruff such a preference cannot exist because of the lack of elaborate aerial displays. Also, reversed sexual dimorphism might be due to differences between females and males in optimal size, related to the parental roles of producing and incubating eggs. In contrast, optimal size in male Ruffs is not limited by parental roles. Inter-individual variation in visual characteristics in the Ruff probably evolved for mutual recognition, the more so as the species cannot use sounds for this purpose. The importance of mutual recognition among resident males is supported by the finding that intruding males prefer residences of males resembling themselves as sites to establish themselves on a lek. Individual recognition of satellites seems to be less important: they can easily be recognized as a class, and inter-individual variation among satellites is much smaller than among independent males.

5.4 The ancestors and their contrasting social lives

There are at least two different ways in which to approach the problem of the origin of the Ruff's social organization. Usually, the assumption is made that the most common type of social organization within a group of related species is the most likely candidate for the type of social organization of their common ancestor. By this reasoning, the common ancestor should have had monogamous pair-bonds and biparental care of the offspring. The alternative approach begins with the variety of types of social organization among the members of a group of related species, and is aimed at the construction of the most plausible evolutionary pathways between these species and their common ancestor. This implies that phylogenetic relationships between the species, and environmental conditions in the past, are also considered (see Section 5.1 and Figure 40). I want to follow this latter line of reasoning.

Earlier in this book I explained that almost any type of social organization may occur among the relatives of the Ruff (see Table 24). I wondered why this variety is much greater than among most other taxonomic groups. Two possibilities may be considered. First, during the evolution of the Scolopacidae, and in particular of the Calidridinae, *selective forces might have been highly variable*. This possibility is not unlikely, given that the ancestral representatives of this group had to invade cold and very cold breeding areas during their evolution (see Section 5.1). This does not exclude the second possibility, namely that the common ancestor of this group might have displayed a very primitive type of social organization with the *potential for evolving many types of derived patterns*. In contrast, the common ancestors of most other groups would have developed types of social organization with fewer options for further specialization. This second possibility implies that certain types of social organization can easily be modified by natural selection, whereas other types can hardly be modified at all. Thus, species with the former types can readily adapt to changing environmental

conditions, but species in the second category may be doomed to extinction after environmental changes. I shall try to explain this with the help of some examples, but first I must give a few more details about another remarkable mating system: double clutching.

Double clutching

In at least three calidridine sandpipers, the Sanderling, Temminck's Stint, and Little Stint, the female may lay two clutches of eggs. The first one is incubated and cared for by the male, and the second by the female. Intervals between clutches are of the order of a few days. Full accounts are given by David Parmelee, Olavi Hildén, Torgrim Breiehagen and Kistchinskij and Flint. The female usually pairs in rapid succession with two males, occasionally three, on different territories, and lays one clutch on each. Usually the male also pairs successively with two females, but only on one territory, his own. The first bond seems to be best described as a short-lasting monogamous pair-bond which is established immediately after arriving in the breeding area, or perhaps even before. After completion of the first clutch, the pair-bond is dissolved. Both male and female resume courtship and copulation activity. Later pairings can hardly be described as bonds: the mating system seems to become promiscuous.

In view of the rapid change of mates by both females and males, the double clutching system seems to be closely related to polyandry and polygyny. The relationship with successive polyandry seems to be especially strong, because some females succeed in laying clutches for two males, and a third one for themselves. There also seems to be a close relationship between monogamy and double clutching. Although the Sanderlings on Bathurst Island in northern Canada did display such a double clutching system, their conspecifics in northeastern Greenland had a monogamous mating system with biparental care, according to Pienkowski and co-workers.

Most probable directions in evolution

The double clutching system involves parental care by only the mother (maternal care), only the father (paternal care), elements of monogamy, and elements of promiscuity. If the environment were to change in such a way that one parent became unable to combine full incubation duties with foraging for self-maintenance, the species could readily evolve a system of biparental care with similar roles for the two parents. If the environment no longer allowed the production of two clutches, the species could evolve a pure paternal care system, or a pure maternal one with competition among males for mates (polygyny, promiscuity, or lekking). If, on the other hand, the environment did allow the production of more than two clutches, the species could evolve a pure paternal care system with competition among females for mates (polyandry). Double clutching therefore seems to leave open a very large number of options for future evolution.

The monogamous mating system involves care by the mother and care by the father, not necessarily equally divided, usually an inability to care alone for a clutch, and the ability to establish a pair-bond. If the environment were to change in such a way that one parent became able to combine full incubation duties with foraging for its own needs, the species could evolve a pure paternal care system or a pure maternal one, combined or not with competition among the members of the non-caring sex. The evolution of a pure paternal care system would also be promoted when the environment allowed the production of more clutches. Thus, monogamous biparental care systems also seem to create a fair number of options for future evolution.

The lekking system of the Ruff includes the ability of the female parent to combine full incubation duties with foraging for her own needs, but no clear ability to establish a lasting bond with a member of the other sex. If the environment of this species changed in such a way that one parent became unable to combine full incubation duties with self-maintenance, the species could not readily evolve a monogamous system with biparental care, and would probably be doomed to extinction. If the environment made possible the production of more than one clutch, the Ruff, again, could not adequately react to take advantage of such a change, and would possibly lose out in competition with other species. Consequently, lekking systems seem to be highly specialized, leaving almost no other options for future evolution.

Viewed in this light, it is highly improbable that the social system of the common ancestor of the Calidridinae, or of the Scolopacidae, could have been similar to the lekking system of the Ruff. It is much more likely that it resembled the monogamous biparental care system, or even the double clutching system. Thus, maternal care in the Ruff and a few other waders seems to be derived from a pattern in which both mother and father cared for offspring, either together or each separately.

Pathways in the evolution of parental care

During my study of the Ruff I became stimulated to reconsider the phylogeny of parental care and social organization in birds. This exercise involved extensive comparisons between species, close examination of their evolutionary pedigree, an analysis of the conditions which may lead to parental care by the mother and to parental care by the father, and comprehensive computer simulations of mating strategies. Surprisingly, this exercise led to a novel hypothesis on the evolution of parental care in birds, in which parental care by the father was considered as the original pattern. By implication parental care by the mother would not have developed in these early stages of evolution, possibly because the increased benefit to the female of an investment in parental care after laying was lower than that of the same investment in egg-reserves. Parental care by the father probably evolved via a stage of mate guarding, by which the male would ensure that his inseminations fertilized the eggs.

It is beyond the scope of this book to deal in detail with this idea. Parts of it have been published already and other parts will be published soon. Here I only want to present an outline of the idea as it has developed until now, without giving all the supporting arguments.

Figure 41 summarizes my model for the most probable pathways for the evolution of parental care and social organization in birds. From an initial stage with pure male parental care and a short-lasting pair-bond, the lineage towards modern shorebirds first developed a uniparental care system, in which the female took over all parental duties only if deserted by the mate. Such a system can easily evolve in three directions. Firstly, it may gradually change into biparental care with similar roles, when one parent cannot do the whole job with sufficient success. Secondly, the uniparental care system may develop towards double clutching when conditions favour egg-production. Thirdly, when inter-male competition becomes important, it may evolve into pure female parental care. Biparental care with similar roles may evolve in various directions, such as biparental care with role differentiation, and, should one parent be capable of the whole job, into male care, and female care. I doubt whether these latter two systems are very likely to develop from a stage in which both parents incubate, and thus are able to control egg temperature very precisely, since they would require considerable physiological adaptation, both in the parents and the egg. In contrast to many others, for instance James Erckmann, I also doubt whether

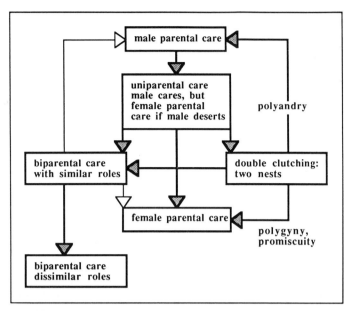

FIGURE 41 *The possible pathways for the evolution of parental care and social organization in waders.*

biparental care evolved into double clutching. Such a process requires the simultaneous development of several properties, such as the ability of a single parent to do the whole job, and the ability of the female to lay two clutches in quick succession. I consider this to be extremely unlikely. Double clutching can easily evolve in three different directions. Firstly, females may become special-ists in laying eggs for different males during successive short-lasting pair-bonds (polyandry). This is incompatible with prolonged female care, and thus the males have to fulfil all parental duties (paternal care). Secondly, it may evolve into biparental care with similar roles, when successful breeding requires more care than a single parent can give. Thirdly, it may also develop into a system in which only the female cares for the offspring (maternal care). Such a situation may occur when inter-male competition becomes important. It may lead to polygyny, promiscuity, and lekking. Whereas biparental care with similar roles may evolve in various directions, female parental care seems to be a dead end, especially when (as in promiscuity and lekking) parents do not maintain any kind of pair-bonding.

Social organization in the Ruff

Double clutching might be considered as the primitive state from which all social systems developed within the Calidridinae. It offers a simple explanation for the evolution of all parental care strategies within the subfamily, and also for all types of pair-bonds. It may even explain the occurrence of alternative mating strategies in males, such as the independent and satellite strategy in the Ruff. The evolution of alternative mating patterns might be the result of the fact that the double clutching strategy enables females to make two different kinds of choices for mates. For the first clutch she should primarily select a male with good caring qualities. For the last clutch she should primarily select a male with good genetic properties to enhance the quality of the offspring.

It is not very likely that in the existing double clutching systems, such as in Temminck's Stints or Sanderlings, females really do make different kinds of decisions for mating between the first and last clutches. If they did, the males with the best genetic properties would probably be more successful by investing in courtship alone than by investing in courtship and parental care. In that case two types of males might arise in the population: caring males, who could be called as *brooders*, and males with superior genes for survival, *competitors*. Such a situation would cause instability of the double clutching system and might ultimately lead to another parental care system. I shall consider a number of reasons for this. Typical brooders may rarely fertilize more than the one clutch they themselves incubate. In contrast, competitors may be able to fertilize all the clutches cared for by females. If the number of caring females was larger than the number of competitors, competitors should be able to fertilize more than one clutch of eggs on average. In that case the proportion of brooders in the population would decrease. If the number of caring females was smaller than the number of competitors, competitors should fertilize less than one clutch on average and the proportion of brooders would increase in the population. A stable situation may arise when the number of competitors equals the number of caring females. Thus, in a population with similar numbers of males and females, such a situation arises when the proportion of competitors equals the proportion of caring females. This would lead to a situation in which all females lay one clutch of eggs. Clutches of some females are fertilized and cared for by brooders, and clutches of the other females are fertilized by competitors and cared for by themselves. If all females care for one clutch of eggs, and the number of males in the population equals the number of females, then competitors should gradually oust brooders. This could result in the evolution of polygynous or promiscuous mating systems without male parental care.

It is conceivable that brooders fertilize more than one clutch of eggs on average, or that their success per clutch is greater than for competitors. It may be possible that females store fertile sperm for considerable periods. A consequence of such a mechanism is that brooders also contribute to the fertilization of second clutches. It is also possible that brooders transfer a more appropriate genotype for parental care to their daughters than competitors. Hence, the former may gain more surviving grandchildren per clutch. As a matter of course, at equilibrium, brooders should get the same number of surviving offspring as competitors. The latter may succeed in this by fertilizing more clutches. Both possibilities imply that, even in a situation with equal numbers of males and females, a female lays more than one clutch of eggs on average. It also follows that the number of brooders is usually lower than the number of females, and thus that some females must care for their first (and last) clutch of eggs.

If the female preference for brooders and competitors leads to a shift from a double clutching system towards a situation in which females usually lay only one single clutch, then a gradual shift towards either pure male or pure female parental care, may also be expected. This does not necessarily result in the extinction of one of the two male strategies. It is conceivable that the brooding strategy, for instance, gradually changes into a sneaky strategy, implying that males, without taking part in inter-male competition, steal copulations from competitors, and perhaps succeed in maintaining the same reproductive success as these competitors. This recalls the Ruff's social system with independent and satellite males. Independent males may be considered as real competitors. Satellite males are certainly not brooders, but they may have been derived from such a group. The differences between the two situations give only limited insights, but it is important to recognize that double clutching has the potential for the evolution of alternative mating strategies in males.

Summary

The Ruff's social organization and parental care pattern is considered to be highly derived. I have suggested that the original breeding pattern in waders resembled double clutching, as shown by Temminck's Stints and Sanderlings, leading to a maximum number of options for the future evolution of derived lifestyles. Double clutching would have evolved from parental care by the father only, which I consider to be the most primitive pattern in birds. Double clutching may even explain the occurrence of alternative mating strategies in males, because the female should theoretically select a male with good caring qualities for the first clutch, while, for the last clutch, genetic properties for survival are more important. This may offer an explanation for the evolution of independent and satellite males in the Ruff.

Epilogue

Ruffs are attractive birds. From an aesthetic point of view, their brilliant colours and impressive communal display provide real pleasure. They are also attractive from a scientific point of view, for many reasons. In the first place, the study of their unique social system provides a great challenge for an ethologist or sociobiologist. Second, the plumage diversity and behavioural dimorphism of the males is fascinating for a geneticist. Third, because of their sexual dimorphism and migratory habits, the species is extremely suitable for biogeographical research. Fourth, because of its unique social behaviour compared to related species, the Ruff prompts theories regarding the evolution of social organization and parental care strategies. The Ruff inspires, provokes wild theories, and sometimes frustrates an investigator with hypotheses that can hardly be tested; but mostly it offers a large measure of scientific satisfaction.

There are many Ruffs in the world, or at least there have been up until now. In western Europe, however, the breeding population of the Ruff has declined drastically during the last few decades. In the Netherlands the number of Ruffs has also decreased since my study near Roderwolde, because modern, large-scale agriculture and Ruffs do not suit each other. The wintering population in Africa is also in great danger; continuous drought and progressive desertification in the Sahel area may lead to the loss of essential winter quarters for the species. Also, hunters take a heavy toll, not only in Africa, but also in the Soviet Union, Italy, France, and even Denmark! The prospects for populations in northern Russia and Siberia are uncertain. I dare not make any prediction about the future of this species, but I am not very optimistic.

Yet I strongly believe that the steps which must be taken to conserve this species must be for the greater good. Similar steps have to be taken as soon as possible to maintain the Sahel area for human habitation. Western Europe is still habitable for humans, but, if nothing is done, the quality of our environment will rapidly deteriorate. A return to a smaller scale agriculture and economy would not be out of keeping with a sustained use of the land by humankind, and with the preservation of the Ruff. Political will is the only requirement!

List of bird names mentioned in the text

Fulmar *Fulmarus glacialis*
Leach's Storm-petrel *Oceanodroma leucorhoa*
Bewick's Swan *Cygnus columbianus*
Lesser Snow Goose *Anser caerulescens*
Mallard *Anas platyrhynchos*
Garganey *Anas querquedula*
Marsh Harrier *Circus aeruginosus*
Willow Grouse *Lagopus lagopus*
Black Grouse *Lyrurus tetrix*
Sage Grouse *Centrocercus urophasianus*
Moorhen *Gallinula chloropus*
Coot *Fulica atra*
Oystercatcher *Haematopus ostralegus*
Black-winged Stilt *Himantopus himantopus*
Avocet *Recurvirostra avocetta*
Ringed Plover *Charadrius hiaticula*
Golden Plover *Pluvialis apricaria*
Grey Plover *Pluvialis squatarola*
Lapwing *Vanellus vanellus*
Surfbird *Aphriza virgata*
Great Knot *Calidris tenuirostris*
Knot *Calidris canutus*
Sanderling *Calidris alba*
Semipalmated Sandpiper *Calidris pusilla*
Western Sandpiper *Calidris mauri*
Red-necked Stint *Calidris ruficollis*
Little Stint *Calidris minuta*
Temminck's Stint *Calidris temminckii*
Long-toed Stint *Calidris subminuta*
Least Sandpiper *Calidris minutilla*
White-rumped Sandpiper *Calidris fuscicollis*
Baird's Sandpiper *Calidris bairdii*
Pectoral Sandpiper *Calidris melanotos*
Sharp-tailed Sandpiper *Calidris acuminata*
Curlew Sandpiper *Calidris ferruginea*
Purple Sandpiper *Calidris maritima*
Rock Sandpiper *Calidris ptilocnemis*
Dunlin *Calidris alpina*
Spoon-billed Sandpiper *Eurynorhynchus pygmeus*
Broad-billed Sandpiper *Limicola falcinellus*
Stilt Sandpiper *Micropalama himantopus*
Buff-breasted Sandpiper *Tryngites subruficollis*
Ruff *Philomachus pugnax*
Great Snipe *Gallinago media*

Black-tailed Godwit *Limosa limosa*
Bar-tailed Godwit *Limosa lapponica*
Whimbrel *Numenius phaeopus*
Curlew *Numenius arquata*
Spotted Redshank *Tringa erythropus*
Redshank *Tringa totanus*
Greenshank *Tringa nebularia*
Wood Sandpiper *Tringa glareola*
Common Sandpiper *Actitis hypoleucos*
Spotted Sandpiper *Actitis macularia*
Turnstone *Arenaria interpres*
Red-necked Phalarope *Phalaropus lobatus*
Grey Phalarope *Phalaropus fulicarius*
Arctic Skua *Stercorarius parasiticus*
Black-headed Gull *Larus ridibundus*
Arctic Tern *Sterna paradisaea*
Black Tern *Chlidonias niger*
Horned Puffin *Fratercula corniculata*
Pied Kingfisher *Ceryle rudis*
White-fronted Bee-eater *Merops bullockoides*
Cock-of-the-Rock *Rupicola rupicola*
Pied Flycatcher *Ficedula hypoleuca*
Great Tit *Parus major*
Pied Wagtail *Motacilla alba*
Harris' Sparrow *Zonotrichia querula*
White-throated Sparrow *Zonotrichia albicollis*
Lapland Bunting *Calcarius lapponicus*

N.B. The above list includes a few species listed in Figure 40 which are not actually mentioned in the text itself.

Selected Bibliography

Altenburg, W., Beemster, N., Van Dijk, K., Esselink, P., Prop, D. and Visser, H. (1985) De ontwikkeling van de broedvogelbevolking van het Lauwersmeer in 1978–83. *Limosa* **58:** 149–161.

Andersen, F.S. (1944) Contributions to the breeding biology of the Ruff (*Philomachus pugnax*). *Dansk Ornith. Foren. Tidsskr.* **38:** 26–30.

Andersen, F.S. (1948) Contributions to the breeding biology of the Ruff (*Philomachus pugnax* (L.)) II. *Dansk Ornith. Foren. Tidsskr.* **42:** 125–148.

Andersen, F.S. (1951) Contributions to the breeding biology of the Ruff (*Philomachus pugnax* (L.)) III. *Dansk Ornith. Foren. Tidsskr.* **45:** 145–173.

Avery, M. and Sherwood, G. (1982) The lekking behaviour of Great Snipe. *Orn. Scand.* **13:** 72–78.

195

Bancke, P. and Meesenburg, H. (1952) A study of the display of the Ruff (*Philomachus pugnax* (L.)). *Dansk Ornith. Foren. Tidsskr.* **46:** 98–109.

Bancke, P. and Meesenburg, H. (1958) A study of the display of the Ruff (*Philomachus pugnax* (L.)) II. *Dansk Ornith. Foren. Tidsskr.* **52:** 118–141.

Beintema, A.J. and Müskens, G.J.D.M. (1987) Nesting success of birds breeding in Dutch agricultural grasslands. *J. Appl. Ecol.* **24:** 743–758.

Beintema, A.J., Beintema-Hietbrink, R.J. and Müskens, G.J.D.M. (1985) A shift in the timing of breeding in meadow birds. *Ardea* **73:** 83–89.

Birkhead, T.R., Atkin, L. and Møller, A.P. (1987) Copulation behaviour of birds. *Behaviour* **101:** 101–138.

Bolze, G. (1969) Anordnung und Bau der Herbst'schen Körperchen im Limicolenschnäbeln in Zusammenhang mit der Nahrungsfindung. *Zool. Anz.* **181:** 313–355.

Bradbury, J.P. (1981) The evolution of leks. pp. 138–169 in: Alexander, R.D. and Tinkle, D.W. (eds) *Natural Selection and Social Behavior.* New York, Chiron Press.

Breiehagen, T. (1989) Nesting biology and mating system in an alpine population of Temminck's Stint *Calidris temminckii. Ibis* **131:** 389–402.

Brodkorb, P. (1967) Catalogue of fossil birds: part 3 (Ralliformes, Ichthyornithiformes, Charadriiformes). *Bull. Fla. State Mus.* **11:** 99–220.

Burton, P.J.K. (1974) *Feeding and the Feeding Apparatus in Waders.* London, British Museum.

Cade, W.H. (1981) Alternative male strategies: genetic differences in crickets. *Science* **212:** 563–564.

Castelijns, H., Marteijn, E.C.L., Krebs, B. and Burggraeve, G. (1988) Overwinterende Kemphanen *Philomachus pugnax* in ZW–Nederland en NW–België. *Limosa* **61:** 119–124.

Christoleit, F. (1924) Zum Balzspiel des Kampfläufers. *Zoologica Palaearctica (Pallasia)* **1:** 181–197.

Clutton-Brock, T.H., Guinness, F.E. and Albon, S.D. (1982) *Red Deer: the Behavior and Ecology of Two Sexes.* Chicago, Chicago University Press.

Cooke, F. and Cooch, F.G. (1968) The genetics of polymorphism in the Snow Goose *Anser caerulescens. Evolution* **22:** 289–300.

Cracraft, J. (1981) Towards a phylogenetic classification of the recent birds of the world (class *Aves*). *Auk* **98:** 681–714.

Cramp, S. and Simmons, K.E.L. (eds) (1982) *The Birds of the Western Palearctic*, Vol. III. Oxford, Oxford University Press.

Davidson, N.C. (1983) Formulae for estimating the lean weight and fat reserves of shorebirds. *Ringing Mig.* **4:** 159–166.

Davidson, N.C. (1984) How valid are flight range estimates for waders? *Ringing Mig.* **5:** 49–64.

Davidson, N.C. and Pienkowski, M.W. (eds) (1987) *The Conservation of International Flyway Populations of Waders.* Wader Study Group Bull. 49, Suppl./IWRB Special Publ. 7.

Davies, N.B. and Houston, A.I. (1981) Owners and satellites: the economics of territory defence in the Pied Wagtail, *Motacilla alba. J. Anim. Ecol.* **50:** 157–180.

De Jonge, J. and Videler, J.J. (1989) Differences between the reproductive biologies of *Tripterygion tripteronotus* and *T. delaisi* (Pisces, Perciformes, Tripterygiidae): the adaptive significance of an alternative mating strategy and a red instead of a yellow nuptial colour. *Mar. Biol.* **100:** 431–437.

De Vos, G.J. (1979) Adaptedness of arena behaviour in Black Grouse (*Tetrao tetrix*) and other grouse species (Tetraonidae). *Behaviour* **68**: 227–314.

De Waal, F.B.M. (1982) *Chimpanzee Politics*. London, Jonathan Cape.

Dobrinskij, L.N. (1969) The analysis of the variations in the populations of Ruff (*Philomachus pugnax* L.) (in Russian). *Trudy Inst. ekol. rasten, zhiv. Akad. Nauk SSSR Ural. Fil.* **71**: 85–96.

Dobrinskij, L.N. (1970) An attempt of colometric estimation of colour in polymorphic species of birds (in Russian). *Zool. Zjurn.* **49**: 1543–1547.

Dominey, W.J. (1980) Female mimicry in male Bluegill Sunfish – a genetic polymorphism? *Nature* **284**: 546–548.

Drenckhahn, D. (1968) Die Mauser des Kampfläufers, *Philomachus pugnax*, in Schleswig–Holstein. *Corax* **2**: 130–150.

Drenckhahn, D. (1973) Zur Beteiligung männlicher Kampfläufer, *Philomachus pugnax*, an der Brutpflege. *Corax* **4**: 147–150.

Drenckhahn, D. (1975) Das Prachtkleid männlicher Kampfläufer (*Philomachus pugnax*). *Corax* **5**: 102–113.

Emlen, S.T. (1976) Lek organization and mating strategies in the Bullfrog. *Behav. Ecol. Sociobiol.* **1**: 283–313.

Emlen, S.T. (1981) Altruism, kinship, and reciprocity in the White-fronted Bee-eater. pp. 217–230 in: Alexander, R.D. and Tinkle, D.W. (eds) *Natural Selection and Social Behavior*. New York, Chiron Press.

Emlen, S.T. and Oring, L.W. (1977) Ecology, sexual selection and the evolution of mating systems. *Science* **197**: 215–223.

Erckmann, W.J. (1983) The evolution of polyandry in shorebirds: an evaluation of hypotheses. pp. 113–168 in: Wasser, K. (ed.) *Social Behavior of Female Vertebrates*. New York, Academic Press.

Falls, J.B. (1969) Functions of territorial song in the White-throated Sparrow. pp. 207–232 in: Hinde, R.A. (ed.) *Bird Vocalizations. Their Relation to Current Problems in Biology and Psychology*. Cambridge, Cambridge University Press.

Ferri, L.V. (1939) Analysis of polymorphism among male Ruffs *Philomachus pugnax* L. (in Russian, cited by Dobrinskij, 1969). *Tr. Tomsk. med.* **11**.

Ficken, R.W., Ficken, M.S. and Hailman, J.P. (1978) Differential aggression in genetically different morphs of the White-throated Sparrow (*Zonotrichia albicollis*). *Z. Tierpsychol.* **46**: 43–57.

Gadgil, M. (1972) Male dimorphism as a consequence of sexual selection. *Am. Natur.* **106**: 574–580.

Gibson, D.D. (1977) First North American nest and eggs of the Ruff. *Western Birds* **8**: 25–26.

Glutz Von Blotzheim, U.N., Bauer, K.M. and Bezzel, E. (eds) (1975) *Handbuch der Vögel Mitteleuropas*, Band 6. Wiesbaden, Akademische Verlagsgesellschaft.

Goethe, F. (1953) Färbungtypen männlicher Kampfläufer aus den Pripet-Sümpfen. *Vogelring* **22**: 43–47.

Harengerd, M. (1982) *Beziehungen zwischen Zug und Mauser beim Kampfläufer, Philomachus pugnax (Linné 1758, Aves, Charadriiformes, Charadriidae)*. Inaugural Dissertation, Bonn.

Hatch, S.A. (1983) Mechanism and ecological significance of sperm storage in the Northern Fulmar with reference to its occurrence in other birds. *Auk* **100**: 593–600.

Heinroth, O. and Heinroth, M. (1927/28) *Die Vögel Mitteleuropas*, Band 3. Berlin, Bermühler.

Hildén, O. (1975). Breeding system of Temminck's Stint *Calidris temminckii*. *Orn. Fenn.* **52**: 117–146.

Hogan-Warburg, A.J. (1966) Social behavior of the Ruff, *Philomachus pugnax* (L.). *Ardea* **54**: 109–229.

Höglund, J. and Lundberg, A. (1987) Sexual selection in a monomorphic lek-breeding bird: correlates of male mating success in Great Snipe *Gallinago media*. *Behav. Ecol. Sociobiol.* **21**: 211–216.

Ivanova, N.S. (1973) Postembryonic development in the Ruff (*Philomachus pugnax*) (in Russian). *Zool. Zjurn.* **52**: 1677–1682.

Ivanova, N.S. (1973) Reproductive biology of the Ruff (in Russian). *Vestnik Leningr. Univ.* **15** (3): 26–29.

Järvi, T. and Bakken, M. (1984) The function of the variation in the breast stripe of the Great Tit, *Parus major*. *Anim. Behav.* **32**: 590–596.

Jehl, J.R. (1968) *Relationships in the Charadrii (Shorebirds): A Taxonomic Study Based on Colour Patterns of the Downy Young*. San Diego Soc. Nat. Hist. Memoir 3.

Jehl, J.R. and Murray, B.G. (1986) The evolution of normal and reverse sexual size dimorphism in shorebirds and other birds. pp 1–86 in: Johnson, R.F. (ed.) *Current Ornithology*, vol. 3. New York, Plenum Press.

Khlebosolov, E.I. (1989) Mechanisms of nesting density regulation and adaptive significance of the lek mating system in Ruff (*Philomachus pugnax*) (in Russian). *Zool. Zjurn.* **68**: 77–88.

Kistchinskij, A.A. (1976) Quantification of the biomass of birds and the conversion of energy by birds in the subarctic ecosystem (in Russian). *Ekologija* **5**: 71–78.

Kistchinskij, A.A. and Flint, V.E. (1973) A case of 'double nesting' in the Little Stint *Calidris minuta* (in Russian). pp. 56–57 in: *Fauna and Ecology of Waders*, vol. I. Moscow, Moscow University Press.

Kistchinskij, A.A. and Flint, V.E. (1973) Contributions to the biology of the Ruff in the Jana and Indirga lowlands (in Russian). pp. 57–60 in: *Fauna and Ecology of Waders*, vol. I. Moscow, Moscow University Press.

Kondratiev, A.Ja. (1982) *Biology of Waders in Tundras of Northeast Asia* (in Russian). Moscow, Akademia Nauk SSSR.

Koopman, K. (1986) Primary moult and weight changes of Ruffs in The Netherlands in relation to migration. *Ardea* **74**: 69–77.

Koopman, K., Piersma, T., Timmerman, A. and Engelmoer, M. (1982) Eerste verslag van de steltloperringgroep F.F.F. over de periode 1 juli 1980–31 december 1981, met speciale aandacht voor Kemphaan en Tureluur. *Twirre*, Speciaalnummer.

Kvaerne, M. (1970) Observasjoner fra Brushanenes spillplasser pa Fokstumyra 1969. *Sterna* **9**: 22–27.

Lank, D.B. and Smith, C.M. (1987) Conditional lekking in Ruff (*Philomachus pugnax*). *Behav. Ecol. Sociobiol.* **20**: 137–145.

Larson, S. (1957) The suborder Charadrii in arctic and boreal areas during the tertiary and pleistocene. A zoogeographic study. *Acta Verteb.* **1**: 1–84.

Lemnell, P.A. (1978) Social behaviour of the Great Snipe *Capella media* at the arena display. *Ornis Scand.* **9**: 146–165.

Lindemann, W. (1951) Ueber die Baltzerscheinungen und die Fortpflanzungs–biologie beim Kampfläufer (*Philomachus pugnax* L.). *Z. Tierpsychol.* **8**: 210–224.

MacLean, S.F. and Pitelka, F.A. (1971) Seasonal patterns of abundance of tundra arthropods near Barrow. *Arctic* **24**: 19–40.

Mickevich, M.F. and Parenti, L.R. (1980) Review of: *The Phylogeny of the Charadriiformes* by J.G. Strauch. *Syst. Zool.* **29:** 108–113.

Mildenberger, H. (1953) Zur Fortpflanzungsbiologie des Kampfläufers (*Philomachus pugnax* L.). *J. Orn.* **94:** 128–143.

Morel, E. and Roux, F. (1973) Les migrateurs Palaearctiques au Senegal: notes complimentaires. *Terre et Vie* **27:** 523–545.

Morris, D. (1952) Homosexuality in the Ten–spined Stickleback (*Pygosteus pungitius* L.). *Behaviour* **4:** 233–261.

Myers, J.P. (1979) Leks, sex, and Buff-breasted Sandpipers. *Am. Birds* **33:** 823–824.

Myers, J.P. (1981) Cross–seasonal interactions in the evolution of sandpiper social systems. *Behav. Ecol. Sociobiol.* **8:** 195–202.

Myers, J.P. (1981) A test of three hypotheses for latitudinal segregation of the sexes in wintering birds. *Can. J. Zool.* **59:** 1527–1534.

Myers, J.P. (1982) The promiscuous Pectoral Sandpiper. *Am. Birds* **36:** 119–122.

O'Donald, P. and Davis, P.E. (1959) The genetics of the colour phases of the Arctic Skua. *Heredity* **13:** 481–486.

Oring, L.W. (1964) Displays of the Buff-breasted Sandpiper at Norman, Oklahoma. *Auk* **81:** 83–86.

Ornithologische Arbeitsgemeinschaft Münster (1989) Beobachtungen zur Heimzugstrategie des Kampfläufers *Philomachus pugnax. J. Orn.* **130:** 175–182.

Parmelee, D.F. (1970) Breeding behavior of the Sanderling in the Canadian high arctic. *Living Bird* **9:** 97–146.

Parmelee, D.F. and Payne, R.B. (1973) On multiple broods and the breeding strategy of arctic Sanderlings. *Ibis* **115:** 218–226.

Pearson, D.J. (1981) The wintering and moult of Ruffs *Philomachus pugnax* in the Kenyan Rift Valley. *Ibis* **123:** 158–182.

Pienkowski, M.W. and Green, G.H. (1976) Breeding biology of Sanderlings in northeast Greenland. *Br. Birds* **69:** 165–177.

Pienkowski, M.W. and Greenwood, J.J.D. (1979) Why change mate? *Biol. J. Linn. Soc.* **12:** 85–94.

Piersma, T. (ed.) (1986) *Breeding Waders in Europe. A Review of Population Size Estimates and a Bibliography of Information Sources.* Wader Study Group Bull. 48, Suppl.

Pieters, A.L., Van Sijpveld, C.W. and Van Orden, C. (1967) Kemphaanwetenswaardigheden. *De Levende Natuur* **70:** 55–60.

Pitelka, F.A., Holmes, R.T. and MacLean, S.F. (1974) Ecology and evolution of social organization in arctic sandpipers. *Am. Zool.* **14:** 185–204.

Portielje, A.F.J. (1931) Versuch zu einer verhaltungsphysiologischen Deutung des Balzgebarens der Kampfschnepfe. *Philomachus pugnax* (L.). *Proc. VIIth Int. Orn. Congr. Amsterdam*, pp. 156–172.

Reyer, H.-U. (1980) Flexible helper structure as an ecological adaptation in the Pied Kingfisher (*Ceryle rudis*). *Behav. Ecol. Sociobiol.* **6:** 219–227.

Reynolds, J.D. (1984) Male Ruff displays to three females near Churchill, Manitoba. *Blue Jay* **42:** 219–221.

Rohwer, S. (1975) The social significance of avian winter plumage variability. *Evolution* **29:** 593–610.

Rohwer, S. and Rohwer, F.C. (1978) Status signalling in Harris Sparrows: experimental deceptions achieved. *Anim. Behav.* **26:** 1012–1022.

Røskaft, E., Järvi, T., Bakken, M., Bech, C. and Reinertsen, R.E. (1986) The relationship between social status and resting metabolic rate in Great Tits (*Parus major*) and Pied Flycatchers (*Ficedula hypoleuca*). *Anim. Behav.* **34**: 838–842.

Salomonson, F. (1955) The evolutionary significance of bird migration. *Det. Kongelige Danske Videnskabernes Selskap, Biologiske Meddelelser* **22**: 1–62.

Scheufler, H. and Stiefel, A. (1985) *Der Kampfläufer.* Neue Brehm-Bücherei. Wittenberg, Ziemsen.

Schlegel, H. (1861) *Natuurlijke Historie van Nederland. De Vogels.* Haarlem, Kruseman.

Schmitt, M.B. and Whitehouse, P.J. (1976) Moult and mensural data of Ruff on the Witwatersrand. *Ostrich* **47**: 179–190.

Scott, D.K. (1978) Identification of individual Bewick's Swans by bill patterns. pp. 160–168 in: Stonehouse, B. (ed.) *Animal Marking: Recognition Marking of Animals in Research.* London, MacMillan Press Ltd.

Segre, A., Richmond, R.C. and Wiley, R.H. (1970) Isozyme polymorphism in the Ruff (Aves: *Philomachus pugnax*): A species with polymorphic plumage. *Comp. Biochem. Physiol.* **36**: 589–595.

Selous, E. (1906–1907) Observations tending to throw light on the question of sexual selection in birds, including a day-to-day diary on the breeding habits of the Ruff (*Machetes pugnax*). *Zoologist* **10**: 201–219, 285–294, 419–428; **11**: 60–65, 161–182, 367–381.

Shepard, J.M. (1975) Factors influencing female choice in the lek mating system of the Ruff. *Living Bird* **14**: 87–111.

Siedel, F. (1960) Am Turnierplatz der Kampfhähne. *Kosmos* **56**: 471–476.

Silverin, B. (1980) Effects of long–acting testosterone treatment on free–living Pied Flycatchers, *Ficedula hypoleuca*, during the breeding period. *Anim. Behav.* **28**: 906–912.

Slagsvold, T. and Lifjeld, J.T. (1988) Plumage colour and sexual selection in the Pied Flycatcher *Ficedula hypoleuca. Anim. Behav.* **36**: 395–407.

Spillner, W. (1971) Das Balzverhalten des Kampfläufers. *Falke* **18**: 148–161.

Strauch, J.G. (1978) The phylogeny of the Charadriiformes (Aves): a new estimate using the method of character compatibility analysis. *Trans. Zool. Soc. Lond.* **34**: 263–345.

Temminck, C.J. (1815) *Manuel d'Ornithologie.* Amsterdam, Sepp.

Thijsse, J.P. (1904) *Het Vogeljaar.* Amsterdam, Versluys.

Trail, P.W. (1985) Courtship disruption modifies mate choice in a lek–breeding bird. *Science* **227**: 778–780.

Tréca, B. (1975) Les oiseaux d'eau et la riziculture dans le delta du Sénégal. *L'Oiseau et R.F.O.* **45**: 259–265.

Tréca, B. (1983) L'influence de la sécheresse sur le rythme nycthemeral des Chevaliers Combattants *Philomachus pugnax* au Sénégal. *Malimbus* **5**: 73–77.

Turner, E.L. (1920) Some notes on the Ruff. *Br. Birds* **14**: 146–153.

Van den Assem, J. (1967) Territory in the Three-spined Stickleback, *Gasterosteus aculeatus* L., an experimental study in intra–specific competition. *Behaviour* Suppl. 16: 1–164

Van Dijk, G. (1983) De populatie-omvang (broedparen) van enkele weidevogelsoorten in Nederland en de omringende landen. *Het Vogeljaar* **31**: 117–133.

Van Dinteren, G. (1987) *Trekgedrag, Verspreiding en Overlevingskansen van Kemphaantjes Philomachus pugnax.* RIN-Report.

Van Eerden, M.R., Prop, J. and Veenstra, K. (1979) De ontwikkeling van de broedvogelbevolking in het Lauwersmeergebied sinds de afsluiting in 1969 t/m 1976. *Limosa* **52**: 176–190.

Van Oordt, G.J. and Junge, G.C.A. (1934) The relation between the gonads and the secondary sexual characters in the Ruff (*Philomachus pugnax*). *Acta Soc. Biol. Latviae* **4:** 141–145.

Van Oordt, G.J. and Junge, G.C.A. (1936) Die hormonale Wirkung der Gonaden auf Sommer– und Prachtkleid. III. Der Einfluss der Kastration auf männliche Kampf-läufer (*Philomachus pugnax*). *Wilhelm Roux' Arch. Entwicklungsmech. Org.* **134:** 112–121.

Van Rhijn, J.G. (1973) Behavioural dimorphism in male Ruffs *Philomachus pugnax (L)*. *Behaviour* **47:** 153–229.

Van Rhijn, J.G. (1983) On the maintenance and origin of alternative strategies in the Ruff *Philomachus pugnax. Ibis* **125:** 482–498.

Van Rhijn, J.G. (1984) Phylogenetical constraints in the evolution of parental care strategies in birds. *Neth. J. Zool.* **34:** 103–122.

Van Rhijn, J.G. (1985) A scenario for the evolution of social organization in Ruffs *Philomachus pugnax* and other charadriiform species. *Ardea* **73:** 25–37.

Van Rhijn, J.G. (in press) Unidirectionality in the phylogeny of social organization, with special reference to birds. *Behaviour.*

Van Rhijn, J.G. (in press) Mate guarding as a key factor in the evolution of parental care in birds. *Anim. Behav.*

Van Winden, A., Mosterd, K., Ruiters, P., Siki, M. and De Waard, H. (1979) Waders and waterfowl in spring 1988 at Eber Gölü, Turkey. The importance of freshwater lakes, in the western part of Anatolia, Turkey, for migrating waders and waterfowl in spring, with special reference to Ruffs (*Philomachus pugnax*). WIWO Report Nr. 28.

Von Frisch, O. (1959) Zur Jugendentwicklung, Brutbiologie und vergleichenden Etholo-gie der Limicolen. *Z. Tierpsychol.* **16:** 545–583.

Whitfield, D.P. (1986) Plumage variability and territoriality in breeding Turnstone *Arenaria interpres*: status signalling or individual recognition? *Anim. Behav.* **34:** 1471–1482.

Wirz, P. (1978) The behaviour of the mediterranean *Trypterygion* species (Pisces, Blennioidei). *Z. Tierpsychol.* **48:** 142–174.

Wirz, P. (1981) Territorial defence and territory take-over by satellite males in the Waterbuck *Kobus ellipsiprymnus* (Bovidae). *Behav. Ecol. Sociobiol.* **8:** 161–162.

Index